The Unmarried Sisters

BOOKS BY DALE FIFE

Weddings in the Family

The Unmarried Sisters

DALE FIFE

* THE *

UNMARRIED

SISTERS

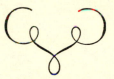

ILLUSTRATED BY LILI CASSEL

Farrar, Straus and Cudahy
New York

FIRST PRINTING, 1958

Copyright © 1958 by Dale Fife
Library of Congress catalog card number 58–12488
Published simultaneously in Canada
by Ambassador Books, Ltd., Toronto
Manufactured in the United States of America
by H. Wolff, New York

DESIGNED BY MARSHALL LEE

TO DUNCAN
for his enthusiasm.
May he never lose it.

CONTENTS

* I *

THE YEAR OF THE

BUTTERFLY

* * *

The year 1915 was almost over, the winter, the spring
and the summer having already been lived, with the
autumn upon us, before Odile went back to the beginning of it in her diary and, in her rather good Palmer
hand, wrote: "The year of the butterfly."

"Why?" I asked, standing over her where she sat
by the window at her newly painted desk in our shared
second floor bedroom. Odile had recently talked Papa
into painting our golden oak bedroom furniture white,

and she had successfully begged for curtains that would tie back from the windows, so that now she seemed to be sitting directly under one of the frost embossed maple trees which towered above our stone house. The room had "grown up." Cleared of jacks, skates and litter, it made me feel younger than my twelve years, and Odile seemed older than her fifteen.

Odile had paid no attention to my question, so I poked her in the back. "Why do you call it the year of the butterfly?"

She turned around, took off her glasses and fixed her steady blue eyes on me. "Shatzie," she said, "if we lived in China you would not ask such a foolish question. There 1915 would not be just a number between 1914 and 1916. In China years have names—the year of the crab, the year of the horse—like identification tags."

"But why the butterfly?" I persisted.

Odile's slender face took on a long-suffering look. "You've heard Papa tell about the cocoon and the butterfly often enough. It's time you learned to figure things out for yourself."

She went back to writing and I was excluded again. I went downstairs, into the living room warmed by the glowing coals of the big base-burner. Papa was standing by the library table opening a box of cigars, for soon the uncles would come. I stood next to him and together we enjoyed the first heady bouquet of the freshly opened tobacco. Papa was a tall, gentle man from the Rhineland of Germany. He had light brown hair and his blue eyes were filled with infinite patience and understanding. Now he put a hand on my head and stroked my hair. "You have something on your mind, Janine?"

I had been ready to ask about the cocoon and the butterfly, but when he called me "Janine" I knew his thoughts were elsewhere. My nickname was "Shatzie," which means sweetheart. Papa almost never called me anything else. I knew Papa was troubled about the yearly gathering this afternoon of both sides of the family—the Alsatian and the German.

"There's nothing on my mind," I said, and I went into the dining room where Helena was sitting in the window seat talking on the telephone. She was giggling, so I knew she was talking with her friend Viola, who was in the same class at the Academy with her. Helena was my pretty sister. She had soft dark hair, impish freckles and brown eyes filled with mischief. Wherever Helena went, there was some boy ready to fall in love with her. At least once a day Helena and Viola talked on the telephone. The conversation was usually about boys. Today was no different ". . . and then he said . . . and then I said . . . and then . . ." I turned away. No use asking Helena.

Mama and Aunt Julie were in the big warm kitchen getting ready for the company. Mama, a white apron over her Sunday green silk, was putting freshly ground coffee, along with a raw egg, into a bag to steep in her largest kettle. She called it "Elsass style" and always made it this way for a crowd. I could see right away that my usually gay, high-spirited mother was in what my father called a "French temper." The iridescent silk of her dress heightened the green of her eyes. Now they blazed at her outburst. "I tell you, Julie, it is a shame the way some of the relatives act because of the war in Europe." She jerked her head angrily and a curl escaped from her smooth, dark pompadour. When my mother was angry, she became a fireball giving off sparks. At such times it was hard to realize she was so small, just five feet, with the slim figure of a young girl.

Aunt Julie nodded her head in agreement as she dusted the freshly baked *Kugelhopfs* with powdered sugar. Julie was my youngest aunt, married to Rousseau Louie, the smart one. She looked like my mother, but she took things much easier. She was, as they said, more *"gemüetlich."* But then, it had been my mother, the eldest of the Ensan family in Alsace, who had undertaken to bring her orphaned brothers and sisters to America to get them out from under hated Bismarckian rule. She had been the vital force that kept this family of German-talking Frenchmen rolling forward to "get to something" in the new land.

I could see that this was not a good time to ask questions, so I took my coat from a hook on the wall and went outside to sit on the back steps. I looked up into the leafless cherry tree, to where a cocoon clung, like a sleeping mouse, colorless against the bare winter branches. I thought of the lowly caterpillar that had spun the cocoon, and I knew that one day a butterfly would emerge from the safe, snug sheath and surprise me with its lovely colors, its grace in flight. But first would come the awkwardness, the uncertainty.

What then had Odile meant by the Year of the Butterfly, as it pertained to the relatives? Had she meant the emergence of the Alsatians—the Ensan family, my uncles Theofil, Florival and Bertie—who had all but lost their humorous Alsatian patois at nightschool and who were now proud citizens? Had she meant Aunt Martha, Uncle Caeser's wife, who had been "the tearful bride" and who at first had hated the city of Toledo, the state of Ohio—in fact all things American—and clung to old country customs, but who now bragged about her modern bungalow? Or once timid Uncle Paulie, who had started with the railroad as a trackwalker, and who had again been promoted, this time to an important job in another city?

Then there were the Germans—the Houcks—Uncle Benedict, my father's youngest brother, who had come to this country at fifteen and had been one of the first to realize that a man might have a good future in the auto business. Perhaps Odile meant Papa, who now did not talk of the beloved hills and forests of his native Germany and who looked sad when the war was mentioned. Or Mama, by nature so militantly French, so anti-Prussian although she spoke with a German accent, and who, against her wishes, had been thrust into the role of peacemaker when German and Alsatian relatives gathered and the wartime policies of Joffre and Von Kluck were hotly argued.

And Odile herself, was she the same headstrong girl who must always learn about life first-hand, and so had gotten us both into many a predicament? Was she the same girl who had walked under the crystal trees with Rudy von Hoffner, and who, on learning that he had been called back to Berlin, had asked shyly: "You'll write?"

We counted the years from Christmas to Christmas in those days—the Christmas we got the astrakhan muffs, the Christmas papa's sister, Aunt Emma, made a cookie tree, the Christmas Eve we were all marooned because of the snow on Cousin Gustave's farm, the Christmas it didn't snow at all. The Year of the Butterfly might be 1915, as Odile had written, but it had its beginnings much earlier, as early as the Christmas of 1912, when Odile championed the Angels of Blossom Street, and she learned that all old people are not necessarily wise. And yet, I think it should begin the November preceding that Christmas, at the Sauerkraut Stomp, because it was that day we first met Rosalie, the girl Uncle Benedict was in love with, for it was Rosalie who taught us many things, and so helped steady the flight of the fumbling butterflies.

* II *

HALLI, HALLO

* * *

The aunts were matchmaking again. My Alsatian and German aunts might not always see eye to eye on this or that subject, but today they were in agreement. Uncle Benedict must surely not be using his head if he had any idea of marrying "that Rosalie."

We were out at Cousin Gustave's farm. Always in the autumn when the red gold leaves on the tall maples around our house were almost but yet not quite finished with their drifting from the trees, when geese honked in patterned southward flight, gray on grayer sky, when each succeeding day brought heavier frost, but still the snows were marking time, there would come a day when my father's cousin, Gustave, would send the word from his big farm three miles out on the Pickle Road, close by the Pickle Woods, that it was time to kill the fattest hog and to make the sausage and the sauerkraut. It was the signal for the yearly two-day reunion of German and Alsatian relatives.

The actual butchering and hanging was done on the first day. This was an age when work was divided according to sex. On this day on Cousin Gustave's farm, men were men and attended to the butchering and to affairs of the smokehouse. It was on the second day that the women sat around the table in the summer kitchen and cut slabs of pork fat into small bits, some to be melted in large cauldrons close by the smoke-house, some to be rendered in big black spiders on the coal oil stove in the porchlike summer kitchen. In the kitchen proper, on the big wood range, the dinner was cooking. This afternoon would come what we called "company relatives"—those not quite at the heart of the family circle.

In the summer kitchen the women, wearing white high-bibbed aprons, were enjoying their role as usual. When had they a better opportunity to sum up the affairs of the past year? Telephones being considered a luxury, this was the way the news was spread about relations in this country and those still on the other side. Already they had exhausted their favorite topic—

who was keeping steady company among the single ones, and would anything come of it? "I hear Amalie walks out with Rimbach Seppie from Mulhausen. Oh Yerra! Could she not do better?"

They had discussed the newly married and learned who was in "an interesting condition." Letters from relatives in Alsace and in Germany had been read, and over the clicking knives worries were brought into the open, incised, dismembered, even as the fat on the cutting board.

Not so easy to dispense with were the problems brought on by the ways of the second generation children. "*Ach! Die kinder*," they sighed. "It was easier in the old country."

My mother, quick in everything she did, was the first to carry her cutting board, with its snowy mountain of cubed fat, to the heating spiders. "Where is Odile?" she asked as she passed behind my chair.

"She's not feeling good," I said. "She went down to the creek."

Aunt Nace's head popped up. "Oh Yerra!" she cried. Nace was not really an aunt. Her husband, Baptiste, was a distant relative. He did the hiring at the railroad shops where many of the relatives, both German and Alsatian, got their first jobs in America. This gave Nace the idea that she was the social leader of the East Side, and in some respects she was. Nace was a skimpy woman with sharp eyes and mousy hair pulled tightly away from her face and twisted into a figure eight atop her head. "Oh Yerra!" she said again.

"So Odile is not feeling good. And why has she the turned stomach? I tell you why. Because yesterday she is the only girl who must be outside with the men while they butcher. Instead of observing how Gustave scalds the pig, how he cuts the liver, what he does with this and that from the animal, she should be inside with the women. Why must she know more about everything than anyone else?"

"She writes things in her diary," I said.

"What could one write in a diary about a butchering?"

I glanced at my mother. Her eyes were glinting as she deftly skimmed crusty bits of fat off the rendered lard in the skillet. No matter if Nace's husband was important, my mother could be trusted to take just so much from her. "We have other things to concern ourselves with," she said in a tone which stopped the conversation about Odile.

Eyes met across the table. I thought I knew what the aunts were thinking. "Is Uncle Benedict really going to marry Rosalie?" I asked.

Tante Emma, my father's sister, came in from the kitchen proper, where the German women were preparing the dinner, in time to hear my question. "Ach, my poor brother Benedict," she moaned.

Emma was a rosy-cheeked woman with hair the color of warm honey. She had the softest heart of any of the aunts. She was also the best cook. "Ach!" she moaned again, all the while brushing melted butter on the rising coffee cakes in the warming oven. "My poor Benedict. A widower at twenty-nine with two small children. We have been talking in the kitchen. Why is it he does not court a good, strong German girl? Why is it he walks out with this Rosie?"

"Not Rosie, Aunt Emma. Rosalie," I said.

The aunts looked with sympathy at Emma. After all it was she who was looking after Benedict's orphaned children. She was raising them with her own four little ones in the house in back of her husband Albert's mattress factory on Main Street on the East Side. Albert, a steady, hard-working man, did not make much money. This was because he made his mattresses so good he couldn't realize enough profit. But Emma was such a good manager and such a good cook that it really didn't seem to matter. Uncle Benedict said that Emma could make a better meal out of a piece of soup meat than most women could with a filet of beef. For some time now, Emma and the women on both the Alsatian and the German sides of the family had tried their hand at matchmaking for "poor Benedict." The girls they proposed had been strong, broad-hipped and mature. One could, after all, not expect a young, inexperienced girl to raise two children belonging to a former wife. This Rosalie Weber was not only young, she was reputed to be on the delicate side. That she came from a fine, upstanding West Toledo family of good German background was admitted. Still she had been born in this country, which meant she must be spoiled, was not a good housekeeper and, as Uncle Florival put it, "had been born with a can opener in her fist."

Aunt Marthe, Uncle Caeser's wife, cherry cheeked, a little dumpy in her oversize coverall apron, was pouring melted fat from one of the spiders into a crock. "I hear that the Webers live on a street of rich homes. Their furniture is said to be solid mahogany, the rugs of finest Axminster. A paid dressmaker makes their clothes."

Heads shook over this information.

My mother looked up from her work at the stove. "No use making up our minds about her yet. Let us wait until this afternoon when Benedict brings her for the dinner."

Emma sighed heavily. "Always it is the sauerkraut stomping I like best thing of whole year. This Rosie will spoil it for me today."

Aunt Julie, finished with her work, poured water from a pitcher into a washbowl which stood on a bench along the wall. "Emma, you are old-fashioned," she said, washing her hands. "You should welcome an American into your family. There are many things for us to learn from those born here."

This statement was greeted in silence, it being quite well agreed, even by my mother, that my youngest aunt and her husband were becoming too modern.

Julie dried her hands on the roller towel, took off her apron and, from a satin-lined crochet bag which hung at her waist, took a bottle of almond lotion and rubbed it into her hands.

"Oh Yerra!" Aunt Nace said under her breath. "It is a wonder she does not sprinkle perfume on the pork."

Julie did not let on she had heard. But she took a small atomizer from her bag and sprayed herself with her favorite "Lily of the Valley" perfume. She gave Nace a look of satisfaction before putting it back into her bag. "By the way, where is Helena?" she asked.

At the mention of Helena the aunts were all ears, she being the eldest niece and so the one to watch for signs of true love. The aunts were romantic. As soon as Helena had made her Confirmation they started embroidering things for her hope chest. They considered all of her boy friends in terms of "possible husbands."

Now I told them that Helena had gone to a football game with a boy from the west side.

Julie clapped her hands. "Football! I hear them shout every Saturday from our house. 'Rah! Zif! Boom! Bah!' I must ask Louie to take me once."

Aunt Nace snorted. "So Helena watches ball-bouncing instead of being here with her relations. Now if I had a daughter, she would be where she is supposed to be."

"She will be here later," my mother said, a little absent-mindedly, as if she were thinking about this morning when she too had thought Helena should be with the relations today, but had finally decided it would be all right if she came later. It seemed strange to me that my mother should worry, for it was to her that the brothers and sisters came with their anxieties. She always seemed to have the right solution for their "first generation" problems. But now it was the second generation that was troubling. I had overheard her talking to my father just this morning. "How are we to know what is right in this country? What are we to say to Helena when she tells us: 'But everyone is going'?"

My father nodded. "In Germany the parents were united on these things."

"And in Alsace there was protection in the set order of tradition," my mother said. "There I knew whether it was right to go to the Kilbe, whether to dance with this one or not." She sighed. "And there is our Odile. She has the crazy ideas. At least so they seem to me. Can I then ask Mrs. Plummer across the street, she who brings her Electra up in what she calls 'twentieth century style' for help? I think not. Paulie's American-born Violetta has good sense, but now they live in Massilon."

My father looked thoughtful. "This is a new country. People worship the new for they have not had time for tradition. In the old country parents are revered. Here the parents revere the children. But the country grows up. The time will come when it will realize the value of things ancient, the lessons to be learned from the past. Until that time, Henriette, we use common sense. I think it works as well in the new country as in the old."

The worry lines had left my mother's forehead as they always did when she talked things out with my father, but now, here in the summer kitchen, I saw that Nace's remark had brought them back.

There was a great shouting outside and Uncle Benedict's eight-year-old Carl, whose mother had been dead now three years, came rushing in. "Henry Hockmaier is here. It's time to make the sausage."

The women tore off their aprons and flew outdoors. The men and the children were already in front of the smokehouse and Henry Hockmaier was the center of attention.

Henry, a bachelor, had come from Papa's village in Germany. His father had been a fine sausage maker and Henry had learned the trade from him. He had come to Toledo with Gustave and his family. Through my father's efforts, he had immediately been hired by a Summit Street butcher. Henry was a broad man with strong shoulders and a proud head. At work, he had bushy eyebrows, sparkling blue eyes and a mustache which curled as high as his cheekbones. He always wore a clean white apron starched as stiffly as cardboard, and sleeve protectors made from butcher paper. Today he had on the same outfit and was already busy with the grinding of the meat and the adding of seasonings.

This was the part we children waited for. For our

benefit, Henry would pretend to make magic signs over the sausage machine. He would put in the ground meat and cry: "Hocus, pocus, dominocus," and—presto—out of the other end of the machine would come fat sausages.

The aunts were watching again to see if Henry was paying attention to Gustave's youngest daughter, Celie. But no, he hardly saw her. Cousin Gustave and his wife, Anna, still insisted that Celie wear middy blouses and pleated skirts and her hair down her back. She did everything she could think of to attract Henry, but nothing worked. Today she was standing with Odile and they were whispering together. No matter how sick Odile might be, she somehow always managed to recover in time for the next act.

As always on this day, Papa and red-necked Cousin Gustave were Henry's helpers. Gustave had a good voice but neither my father nor Henry were much as singers. They had two favorites—*Halli, Hallo* and *O du Lieber Augustin.* Henry sang *Halli, Hallo* in the butcher shop, on picnics, on walks. He whistled it, hummed it, played it on his harmonica. So today, naturally, it was the first song.

After that they swung into *Augustin.* Everyone waited for Uncle Florival to join in. It was always with a great show of pleasure that he tried to drown out the Germans by singing the song in the humorous Alsatian patois. He did it now with rolling eyes and exaggerated gestures: "*O, du liewer Augustin! s'Geld isch hin, All's isch hin!*" But the good-natured sausage makers just kept on singing it in the good old German way while the sausages rolled out of the machine.

Papa looked strange to me wearing one of Henry's white aprons. His eyes always held a faraway look on this day, as if all of this were not happening here, but in distant Baden.

There was the noise of a wagon squeaking over the bridge down by the creek. "It's Deesie," someone cried, and the children ran down the road to meet him.

"He brings the beer," Gustave shouted.

"That one! Oh Yerra!" Nace cried. "Let up hope he does not come with all of it inside him."

We could hear Deesie singing all the way up the hill. As the wagon turned into the farmyard, the bigger boys were hanging onto the back of it while the smaller boys and the girls ran alongside.

Deesie, a little man with a round pink face and curly black hair, liked to sing the sentimental songs of the old country. He brought his team to a halt, stood on the seat, struck a pose and his fine tenor voice rose over the farmyard:

> *"Im Grand' hotel zu Taubensand zitzt*
> *ein Musikverein . . ."*

This was a favorite of everyone—nostalgic, but with a spirited chorus. The uncles forgot their newly acquired sedateness. When Deesie sang *"Das* Piccolo *schreit oben naus,"* Theofil imitated a piccolo player in sound and gesture. Bertie clowned *"Das* Horn, *das will ihm nach,"* and Florival mimicked in *"Die* Tuba *brüllt wie Kuh."*

Everyone swarmed around the wagon for the chorus:

> *"Zi-ne bu-me, zi-ne bu-me, ra-da-da,*
> *Zi-ne bu-me, zi-ne bu-me, hop-sas-sa,*
> *Ti-re-li-re hum-ba-ba,*
> *Düre-le dür-le dür-le zi-nera- da-da,*
> *Bum, bum, bum."*

The song over, the men helped Deesie roll the keg into the basement.

The work of the day was over.

The fun was about to begin.

✳ III ✳

THE SAUERKRAUT STOMP

*　*　*

Gustave's cellar was immense, cool and shadowy. It extended under the entire house and had massive pillars of stone, and small high windows with iron grates. A lantern hung on a beam close by the stairs. The blended flavors of rusticoat apples, winter pears, carrots, turnips and other root vegetables stored in low bins lining the cellar, gave it a homey, earthy fragrance which never failed to fill me with a sense of well-being and plenty.

There were crocks of eggs in waterglass and rows of canned fruits. Ranged against one wall were the wine barrels, their curved sides propped by large stones. Today the center barrel had a spigot in it and alongside stood a table with wine glasses and Gustave's collection of beer mugs.

A pale mountain of cabbage heads stood in the center of the cellar beside a wooden tub over which lay the shredder.

"Now we begin," Gustave announced when everyone was assembled. He took a large cabbage in his strong hands, then slowly, then faster, rhythmically moved it over the cutting blades set slantwise in the wooden cutter. All the while his son, Konrad, kept time on his accordion. Konrad was only fifteen, but he knew all the old tunes. He played "The Henpecked Bridegroom" with such vigor his blond hair fell over his eyes.

> *"Ach Gott ich bin ein armer Mann,*
> *Hab' nickts zu kommandieren;*
> *Die Frau, die hat die Hosen an,*
> *Sie tut das Scepter führen . . ."*

Everybody clapped the chorus:

> *"O jerum, o je-rum, o je-rum, o je!"*

The faster Gustave's hands guided the cabbage, the faster the *"O jerums,"* until the cabbage was finished.

He held up his hands to show there were no scratches or cuts. This was not a job for children. It required skill.

And now it was Uncle Florival's turn. The women kept track to see who would be the fastest this year. Gustave's wife kept the wine glasses filled while Deesie presided over the keg of beer.

Little girl cousins, in clean white aprons and with hands freshly washed, had the job of gathering armfuls of the cabbage and dumping it into the waiting barrel. Little Cousin Carl got to hold the *salz* box this year and, on signal from Aunt Emma, he scattered a handful over the freshly shredded cabbage. When one barrel was filled, another was started. Uncle Theofil cried: "This one is for the Germans," whereupon I got to hold the box labeled *Kümmel* and occasionally scattered the seeds into the barrel.

When three barrels were filled, Gustave shouted to my father: "Herman, it is time to stomp."

Each year Papa took care of this ceremony. As a child in Baden, he had been the village boy chosen by the baron, who lived in the castle on the hill, to stomp the cabbage. From the time he was five until he was ten, he had been invited to the castle at sauerkraut-making time, scrubbed by the servants, put into a white linen suit, and taken down to the cellars where he had stomped the freshly shredded cabbage. Foot stomping was considered the only good method. It was one of the few old-world customs my father retained in this country, and while it was now just a tribute, a few stomps by one of the younger boys, with music added for fun, it remained, for my father, a symbol of his childhood in Germany.

This year Aunt Emma's five-year-old Willie had been chosen to stomp. He was carried in, fresh from the bath, his white cotton suit stiff with starch, his feet bare.

"Now we start," my father said.

"Wait for me. Wait for me." It was Helena flying down the cellar steps. Like my mother, she did everything fast. Long ago she had been nicknamed "Quicksilver" by Father Kelmer, our pastor. She had on a red wool dress and everything about her was bright and gay. Following her, a little self-consciously, was a slim blond boy who looked as if he would rather be any place but here with all these strange people.

Everything stopped while introductions were made. Then there was an uncertain silence. It was one thing to make merry with your own kind, but it was quite another when a stranger came.

There were more steps on the stairs. Uncle Benedict and Rosalie Weber. They had not been expected until suppertime. While the relatives had been curious to see Helena's beau of the day, it was more than curiosity where Miss Weber was concerned. Uncle Benedict was the handsomest of the Houck brothers. He was as tall as my father, which was a little over six feet, and as slender, but where my father was sandy haired, blue eyed and serious, Uncle Benedict had dark hair and brown eyes. He always looked

as if he were just ready to tell a joke. And he usually
was. "What goes on here?" he called out now, descend-
ing the stairs. "I thought today it would be I who
would stomp. Am I not the youngest Houck?"

His children, eight-year-old Carl and the five-year-
old Carrie, came forward shyly. He hugged them
warmly. Rosalie did not "make over" them. She took
Carl by the hand and softly stroked Carrie's hair. The
eyes of the women were on her. They had liked Benedict's first wife. Now they scrutinized the young Rosalie as she was introduced. My mother and her sisters
were friendly. I saw Julie look with interest at the
tweed suit she was wearing. Even I could see it was a
sensible thing to wear on the farm, and that it fit beau-
tifully and was without ornament. Her brown shoes
were polished to shine like satin.

Nace stood off to the side looking as if she were
sniffing for perfume, and Aunt Emma and the other
German aunts seemed unsure as they shook hands. I
liked her. She didn't gush over me, but her handshake
was warm and her lively eyes were full of fun. She was
small, with pert features and shining brown hair. But
it was immediately evident that the German aunts did
not accept her as readily as the Alsatian. After all,
Benedict was one of them. Their glances seemed to
say: "You're friendly. We think we like you, but can
you take care of two children belonging to another
woman? Besides you are American born."

There was an awkwardness, and then I saw Papa
motion to Konrad to start playing. Always the first

song for the sauerkraut stomp was *"Zu Lauterbach hab ich mein strumpf verloren . . ."* because the beat was considered just right for stomping. Papa lifted little Willie into the barrel. He started stomping, slowly at first, the accordion keeping pace with him, going ever faster, faster.

Helena's blond young man stood along the cement wall, wide-eyed. He watched the jumping Willie as if he were a barbarian. Willie was a good jumper. He bounded quite high over the sauerkraut barrel while one song after another was called for.

Uncle Florival called for *"Unser Landl,"* the song which, in patois, extolled the virtues of landmarks close to my mother's home village in Alsace: *"Owa d'Schlessl, 's Düsabachel, 's Bad Carola. Untadra."*

Beer mugs clinked against wine glasses. Uncle Theofil brought forth a treasured bottle of *Kirschewasser*.

Uncle Benedict's Rosalie didn't sing, but her face was animated and she kept time on the cement floor with her slipper.

It took the catchy "Lowlanders Homesickness," and its answer by the "Highlanders" to start the dancing. Florival took a string of garlic from one of the rafters, wound it around his head like a crown and danced around the wine barrel.

"A waltz," someone cried, and Konrad swung into the quick tempo of a European waltz.

Little Willie had meanwhile been lifted from the barrel and carried upstairs on Louie's shoulders.

And then supper was ready, and no one needed to

be called a second time. For once we children didn't
have to wait for second table. Gustave's house was
big and there was room for the children's table in the
summer kitchen.

Supper was always the same on this day. Tureens
of chicken noodle soup cooked by Gustave's wife, and
from Gustave's smokehouse there was ham, tongue
and sausage. On the table too were bowls of cole
slaw with mustard dressing and black bread. "For
last," there was *Apfelkuchen* for which Aunt Emma
had set the dough the day before, punched it down
three times during the night, rolled it out in the morning, spread it with butter, sugar and row on row of
tart apple slices, prunes and nuts, and baked it in
great square pans.

The sauerkraut stomp had been started by my
father to draw together the Alsatian and the German
relatives, for there was always a cleavage between
them. Now that the supper and the singing were over,
it was evident again in the way the Germans gathered
in little circles on one side of the big room and the
Alsatians on the other. This too was the time of day
the children were restless, looking for something new
to do. The older ones, like Helena, were hoping there
would be no more old-fashioned songs. It was in the
evening that the plaintive melodies were sung. I liked
them all—the longing for the homeland, the wander
and the conscript songs. When they sang of the "*heimat*" and of "the sweetheart left behind," I would get
a lump in my throat and almost enjoy being sad.

Helena came to where my mother was sitting with Julie, Nace and Rosalie Weber. "Don wants me to go to a movie," she said, and I looked across the room to see the blond suitor trying to escape from Deesie and one of his long-winded stories.

Mama frowned. "I think it is too early to leave," she said.

"But there's really nothing more to do," Helena said. "Next thing Deesie will get up and tell the story about mending the garbage can—how he innocently picked up a piece of scrap metal on the street, and before he was finished, the entire police force and fire department were in on it. That will take an hour. Then Uncle Florival will tell how he outwitted the whole Prussian army by fleeing the conscript, escaping to France and joining the Foreign Legion. That will make Deesie mad and he'll insist the German army wouldn't have him and that he was in the Legion only because the French considered him a military deserter and thrust him into it. You know how it will go. Before it's over, they'll be waving their arms and shouting."

Nace frowned at Helena. "Why do you not walk out with a good Alsacer boy instead of this sick dog from the West Side? It would seem you are getting the high toned ideas."

Helena looked as if she were going to cry. Odile's chin went out. "Aunt Nace, you're mean . . ."

My mother glanced about her helplessly. Rosalie Weber put out a hand. "I have an idea. May I try it?"

My mother nodded.

Rosalie stood up. She smiled at Helena and Odile. "Benedict has told me much about you girls. I know that you are both good in dramatics. Have you ever done any shadow theater?"

"I've heard of it," Odile said.

"One of my girl friends played it at a party," Helena said.

"Then what do you say we try it?" Rosalie said. "It's fun for everyone, really."

Immediately she was marshaling us into action. "Helena, see if you can borrow an extra large white tablecloth or sheet from Anna, and get your young man to hang it in the wide doorway there between the two pillars. The parlor will do nicely as a stage, and the audience will sit here in the living room. Shatzie, we'll need a lamp placed right here so we can see the figures in shadow behind the cloth." With efficiency and no fuss at all, Rosalie had all of us working.

Rosalie did the first skit, to show us how it was done. When everything was ready, I watched from the living room side. I wasn't allowed to guess what she was portraying because I was in on the secret that it was "Eliza crossing the ice." Rosalie was clever, the way she gestured melodramatically with her arms, and when she hopped from one block of ice to another, I forgot for a minute that she was jumping on pillows. The hail dropping about her was very realistic and didn't look at all like the beans I knew Odile was throwing from the side, and when she cried the cotton balls she had concealed in her fists looked like immense tears.

The children clapped their hands. The grownups didn't know the story of Eliza, but they were interested in the clever shadows. Helena's young man was the first with the right answer, so he got to do the next skit. He chose Helena as his partner. I couldn't figure out what they were doing. There was arm-waving and weeping and falling back into a chair, all with their mouths moving in an exaggerated fashion. It was Uncle Louie who guessed, "The death scene from Camille."

Everyone wanted to do an act. And so the evening passed with laughter, with no little cliques here and there, and no more talk from Helena about leaving early.

Papa, never one for theatricals, took his turn last. He chose me for his partner. He merely walked behind the cloth, leading me by the hand, carrying an alarm clock before him.

"Time to go home," someone guessed, and so it was.

My mother clasped Rosalie's hands when she said good night. She looked up at Benedict. "You will bring her to us to light the Advent wreath?"

Those were the Sundays we made plans for our Christmas festivities. If Mama invited Rosalie, then, as far as she was concerned, Rosalie was already at the heart of the family circle.

* IV *

THE ANGELS OF

BLOSSOM STREET

* * *

My sister Odile's Christmas spirit started to rise with the beginning of the Advent season. By the time the tinseled trees were unveiled in Milner's Department Store windows, her zeal would have soared as high as Aunt Nace's *Kugelhopf* the time she absent-mindedly put in four yeast cakes instead of two. Any moment now Odile would come down with what Uncle Louie called "Santa Claus fever." This year I intended to stay far enough away so as not to catch it. Last year she had involved me in a project of gathering can labels for a contest some enterprising cannery had talked the good nuns into sponsoring. Each label represented votes. The student gathering the most votes was to win twenty-five dollars. The label from a tomato can counted for one vote. Five votes were given for each olive can label, but who ate olives in our neighborhood?

We went up and down the streets, talking housewives into stripping the labels from their canned goods. Asking people for things, even labels, was agony for me, but Odile took me firmly by the hand and said: "Remember we are not asking for ourselves. We will give the twenty-five dollars to the orphanage to buy bananas for Christmas." Since the banana was about the only fruit Odile cared about, she was determined the orphans should enjoy this luxury. "I'm sure no one gives them anything but apples," she said. Odile hated apples.

Although we walked until our feet were sore, and we smarted over many a slammed door, we lost the banana money to a group of eighth-grade boys, headed by Walter Keesling, who had the foresight to bypass the housewives for the city dump. In one afternoon they gathered more labels from empty cans than we had in our week of door-knocking. Odile had called the boys "loud mouths." The day after they collected the prize money, when the "loud mouths" appeared in new balmacans of bright red plaid, our defeat was total.

While Odile had concentrated on orphans and bananas last year, the indications this year were that her Santa Claus fever would have something to do with the "old ones." It was Uncle Florival who had said: "To interest Odile, one must be old, or odd, or better, a little of both."

It was true. This year, Odile did have a wide and varied acquaintance among the old people. "Young people have no flavor," she announced to me one day. "They're like gobs of saltless farina."

But old lady Oldham, who lived in a worn-out shingled house, and in the summertime sat in a worn-out backyard among her ancient lilac bushes and pulled on a corncob pipe—Odile thought she did have flavor. I was inclined to agree after one brief tour of her littered shack. I couldn't see what Odile saw in old Oldham, who had chased me one day, waving her crooked cane, shouting: "Shatzie is a thief," when I tried to swipe one lilac blossom. But Odile would come away with bunches as big as washtubs and old Oldham whining after her: "Come again dearie. There's more."

When I complained to Odile about the treatment I had received, she said: "Serves you right. You don't visit old Oldham for lilacs."

"What for then?"

"Because she's probably the only woman you'll ever know who smokes a corncob. She's part of something going away forever."

As far as I could see, it was good riddance.

This winter Odile had made friends with all the old people at the Little Sisters of the Poor. She visited them after vespers on snowy Sunday afternoons in the big hall of the home, where they sat in a large circle wistfully waiting for someone to stop and talk. Odile came home from these excursions with her pockets filled with the hard candy everyone seemed to think the old people liked. "It's hard on their gums," she said.

This particular Sunday afternoon, when Odile came into the kitchen through the back storm porch, I was busy making out a list of all the presents I hoped to get for Christmas. Without taking off her rubbers or her coat and cap, Odile marched over to the calendar which hung next to the wood box. She counted off the days until Christmas. Then she turned, fixed her steady blue eyes on me and announced: "Shatzie, it is nobler to be a giver than a receiver. It will make you glow on Christmas morning. Now there are the old ladies at the home . . ."

I got up and started edging toward the swinging door and the buzz of conversation from around the dining-room table. Always on this last Sunday in Advent, Mama's brothers and sisters would come to sip wine and to eat the traditional *Laekerlis*, cookies made of honey, spices, fruits and almonds, rolled out, "rested" for twenty-four hours before baking, then, while still warm, "painted" with melted sugar. Later, Father Kelmer would honor us with a visit and the Advent wreath would be lighted. Usually only my mother's relations came on this day. This year it was different. Rosalie and Benedict had been invited.

The talk I had heard through the closed door had been of many things, but, as usual, it had gotten around to the children. I heard Aunt Lily: "So many beaux come calling on Helena, now which do you think she picks? Maybe the strong one who inherits his father's plumbing business? No? Then the skinny one who goes on to the university?"

Odile baffled the relatives completely. She could be measured by no known yardstick. It couldn't be said that she took "after this" or "after that" one. Odile was Odile, questioning everything. Because everyone was doing or wearing a certain thing was, to Odile, not a good enough reason why she should do the same. At the present time the girls Odile's age were going to dancing class. Mr. LaFitte, a Frenchman, taught the fox trot, the waltz, the schottische and the Virginia reel over in West Toledo. A new class, by invitation, was to begin after Christmas. Rosalie had told Mama about it. Helena, softly round, pretty and agreeable, was already enrolled as an advanced pupil. Odile, skinny, gawky and strongheaded, would have no part of it.

Odile was Uncle Florival's favorite. He was also her godfather, which gave him the right to be more than interested in her affairs. Being Florival, he exercised his right to the fullest. I had heard him question Mama and Papa about her activities just this afternoon. He had apparently heard Odile come home, for now he pushed open the door and beckoned us into the dining room. He stroked his short, military mustache as he regarded Odile without pleasure. "Why are you not with Helena at sodality meeting this afternoon? The young ladies plan sleigh ride party. It strikes me that all you do is sit with the old ones. Why?"

Odile gazed at her questioners with patience. "They might die tomorrow. Everything they know will then be lost. If I listen, I can save it."

"For why you save it?" Florival shouted.

Mama gave Florival one of her green-eyed looks. "It is well to save the past," she said tartly, but then more softly as she looked at Odile, "still one must not neglect the present."

Papa got up and put an arm around Odile's shoulders. "Age is not always wise, nor youth ignorant."

Rosalie Weber leaned toward Odile. "They say dancing gives a girl grace."

Odile surveyed Rosalie questioningly. "Who are THEY?" she asked.

Uncle Florival threw up his hands in despair. "Oh Yerra!" he cried.

My father changed the subject. "Time it is for Odile and Shatzie to get valises ready if they are to spend few days at Theofil's. He will be here soon and they must be ready."

Odile grasped the opportunity to escape. I ran up the stairs after her. We were happy to be going over on the west side of town for part of our pre-Christmas vacation. Uncle Theofil had to go to Canton for a few days. His wife, pretty, dark-haired Marie, whom Theofil had married in Alsace and brought to this country just a little over a year ago, didn't like staying alone nights with their new baby. She was young and light-hearted. Also trusting. While she was busy with the baby in the daytime, we could roam and explore at will. Once we had even gone to the dump and watched the ragpickers search for treasure.

As for Odile, the thing she liked best was the prospect of seeing the Angels again. Angelica and Angelina Angel were elderly spinsters who lived next door to Uncle Theofil and Aunt Marie. Small and wispy twins, they set forth each morning for their shop on Blossom Street several miles away in the wholesale district, looking indeed like two angels of mercy in their long blue capes, their thin silver braids wound about their heads in skimpy halos.

"Kind women they are," Aunt Marie said to us on the first morning of our visit as we watched them through the kitchen window. "See they go to work as usual, no matter how cold, so girls in wholesale district have place to buy candy and powder. They save their money so next spring they can retire to place they were born, state called Tennessee, where they will rock all day on porch with jasmine climbing. It makes me to weep when I hear them speak of it."

"Oh, let's visit them tonight," Odile said. "Maybe they'll give me a Christmas job in their store."

I had been right about this year's Santa Claus fever. Odile had confided that she hoped to buy Christmas presents for all the old ladies in the home. There were fifty of them. She had, at the moment, two dollars and fifty cents in her bank.

"How about it?" Odile asked. "May we go see the Angels tonight?"

"Ah yes, poor souls," Aunt Marie said, "We go and we take something for their suppers."

The visit was something to look forward to. One could poke about the Angels' living room for hours and still not see all its treasures; the plaster statue of a boy about to swallow three red cherries; the one of a girl with pigeons roosting in her hair. Then there were the pictures of Tennessee—horses romping on Tennessee grass; cows munching in Tennesee pastures; orchards blooming in Tennessee. I could see Tennessee half covering the Union.

Best of all was the large framed bouquet of flowers made from the hair of the Angels' relatives. "Now this yellow daisy," Angelina had once explained. "It grew on Cousin Belinda's head. Folks used to say God never made hair this color and that Belinda had a little help from the devil. Now the brown center of the daisy came from the head of her husband, Beau. Wiry, stiff as a horse brush it was, his hair."

That evening, as soon as we saw the light go on in their house, Aunt Marie had Odile ladle out a quantity of calfshead soup with marrow dumplings, while she bundled up the baby. I took the lead and knocked on the door.

Angelica, the twin with the mole on the left side

of her chin, opened the door, grabbed the soup with one hand and with the other waved us into the room. "Kind, charitable, neighborly neighbors, may you be rewarded in the hereafter," she chanted.

Angelina, the twin with the mole on the right side of her chin, was sitting in a wicker rocker, her coat still on, her hat still perched atop her halo, her feet in a bucket of water. "Such a hard, busy day," she wailed. "The girls in the neighborhood are doing their Christmas shopping. Now if the good Lord will see me through this one last winter, come spring I'll be in Tennessee rocking in the jasmine."

Marie made sympathetic noises. "You should take it more easy."

Angelina stood next to Angelica. "We are glad we can be of service to those who need us, aren't we Angelica?"

They nodded in unison, their pale eyes misty. Aunt Marie was right, I thought. These were indeed good women. Two highborn southern ladies running the store as a sort of charitable institution.

Odile straightened her skinny shoulders. She marched briskly across the room to stand before the Angels. "Have you considered hiring a clerk?" she asked.

The Angels rolled their eyes at each other. "Help is hard to find. Wages high."

"I'd like to make some money before Christmas," Odile said, "I wouldn't charge much. I would charge very little indeed."

The Angels rolled their eyes again. "Too young," they said in unison.

Angelina rubbed her feet with a towel. "Perhaps, Angelica, the kind little girl could help us mornings— with the candy and the perfume."

Angelica looked doubtful. "We are in a poor neighborhood," she explained. "The girls work very hard for the little money their stingy employers pay them. We are boxing candy and filling perfume bottles to sell to them for practically nothing at all, so they can afford to buy a few Christmas presents."

Angelina was putting on her slippers. "There are dozens of candy boxes in the back room to be filled." She sighed. "We will never be able to finish."

"Oh let me help, please," Odile cried. Her eyes were shining and I surmised that, out of necessity, she was ready to switch her charitable impulses from the old ladies to the poor working girls. The warm Christmas glow, I imagined, could be obtained one way as well as another.

Angelica reached over and clasped her sister's hands. "We'd like to hire her, wouldn't we Angelina? Alas, we can't afford to."

"But Shatzie and I will work free," Odile said. "We've been wanting to do something for the old ladies at the Little Sisters of the Poor. Instead we'll help the working girls."

The idea had no appeal for me, but now my Christian spirit tormented me. Did I dare hold out for pay? Of course there'd be candy.

The Angels consulted each other with their eyes. There was a moment of hesitation. Then they nodded.

Everything was quickly settled. We were to walk through the wholesale district until we reached the railroad track that crossed the street from the coffee company yard to the chocolate company yard. A few steps and we would be at their back door. "Mind you don't come in the front way," Angelica admonished.

"Why not?" Odile asked.

"You're too young to work. If the policeman on the street saw you, there would be trouble. He isn't around much until afternoons. You'll go home at one o'clock."

The next morning it was snowing. Over our buckwheat pancakes I suggested we forget the whole idea in favor of making a snowman. Odile didn't even hear me.

It was a long, cold walk. Once in the wholesale district the twin scents of chocolate and roasting coffee gave a delicious mocha flavor to the air. We crossed the track. There, ahead, was the Angels' store. It was a brick building, black with soot.

"Kind, charitable little girls, may you be rewarded in the hearafter for your generosity," Angelica chanted us into the store, while Angelina fluttered about helping us off with coats and rubbers.

They escorted us to a small, windowless room, lighted by a gas mantle and heated with a coal stove. A round table stood in the center of the room. It was piled high with poinsettia decorated candy boxes. My job was to line them with waxed paper while Odile was to fill them with chocolates from large cardboard containers which stood on a side counter and bore the name of a wholesale candy factory we had seen down the street. Some she was to wrap in gold foil.

"You may eat the mashed ones," Angelica said.

Odile and I worked all morning at our task of charity. When we finished a box, one of the Angels would tie a red satin ribbon around it.

"They look pretty," Odile said to me, "but I've tasted better candy."

I had expected that my great work of charity would immediately impart the rosy glow of the giver to me. This I imagined to be an airy sort of condition that would mount and mount until I would be practically floating. But by noon my pay in mashed chocolates had given me only a rocky feeling in the pit of my stomach, completely crowding out any spiritual glow which might have been lurking about.

On the way home the smell of chocolate from the factory down the street hung like a dark brown curtain on the cold air. I shuddered, pulled my muffler up around my nose and plodded, alongside Odile, to Aunt Marie's.

The next day we filled small bottles with perfume, by way of a funnel, from three large jugs. These were marked *Rose, Violet,* and *Carnation.*

"Um, it smells good," Odile said pouring a measure of *Rose* through the funnel.

We were seldom allowed in the store itself "because

of the policeman," but we could peek through cracks
in the wall and see the dim, cluttered aisles. When the
bell rang, announcing a customer through the door,
Odile and I would rush to the cracks. It was usually
a girl from one of the wholesale houses or factories.
We could tell the ones who worked in offices because
they wore green eye shades and black sleeve protectors
and their coats were thrown over their shoulders. The
factory workers wore black sateen aprons under their
coats and some of them spoke broken English. I tried
to see the mark of their cruel employers on their faces,
but was unable to distinguish it and decided I just did
not know human nature.

During the noon hour the girls arrived in groups and
there was a constant chatter and the jingle of the cash
register. When they were gone and the store was
empty again, Angelica and Angelina came in, told us
it was time to go home and helped us with our coats
and hats. I could see they were crestfallen. Odile asked
them what the trouble was.

"The girls don't care for *Rose* and *Violet* and *Carnation* perfume this year. We're overstocked. They all
want a new perfume called *Forbidden*, just because it's
supposed to be the favorite scent of Theda Bara."

Odile and I sympathized with the Angels. We were
indignant at the girls for being so unkind, considering
the Angels were devoting their lives to them.

That night we told Aunt Marie about the perfume.
Soft-hearted Marie almost wept. "Poor old ladies. I
buy a bottle of their perfume. Tonight I take them

supper again." By this time Marie was cooking as much for the Angels as she was for us.

The next morning while we worked, Angelina rushed into the back room, eyes bulging. "Ssh. Policeman." She fluttered out.

Odile tiptoed to the cracks. "There's a patrol wagon outside," she whispered. "I can see it through the window."

I held my breath. My heart pounded. This was thrilling. How wonderful it was to be a giver.

Now we no longer filled perfume bottles. We spent the time packing candy boxes and eating mashed chocolates for four mornings. The fourth night I couldn't eat my dinner and Odile was sick. Also, Uncle Theofil was home.

When he heard what we had been doing, he was angry with Aunt Marie. "Charity is charity, and I would be the first to say the girls could help. But to work long hours and so far from this house, I am surprised, Marie, that you would allow it. Good thing I come back. I take them home tonight."

Odile argued that we had not finished packing the candy, but once Uncle Theofil made up his mind to something, there was no budging him.

So we were home once more and we hadn't earned any money. Odile emptied her bank. The coins made a small pile atop her bed. She counted. They still came to only two dollars and fifty cents. "Just enough to buy presents for the family," she said. "I did want to get something for the old ladies."

The next day we got permission to cross over the Cherry Street bridge to Christmas shop on Summit Street. We bought a vase for Mama, a stickpin for Papa and a lavalier for Helena.

When we were finished it was still early and Odile said: "Let's go see the Angels. We never did explain to them why we didn't finish our job."

"It's too far to walk in the cold," I protested.

"We're not working now. We don't have to be afraid of the policeman. We can take the streetcar, the way the Angels do every morning, and get off right at Blossom Street. We'll have only one block to walk."

We ran across the street and jumped on a car. It had begun to snow again. The Christmas tree lights in the stores winked at us through the mobile curtain of snow. My hands were warm in my muff, the fur around my neck was snuggly and smooth and smelled just a little of moth balls. Christmas is the most wonderful time of the year, I thought, and I dreamed of all the presents I would get. And then the conductor was calling "Blossom Street," and we climbed up the icy steps of the streetcar and walked down the bleak street toward the Angels' store. When we reached it we stood for a moment peering through the frosty windows. I heard Odile gasp. "Look," she cried, pointing. There were some of the candy boxes we had filled. There too were some of the perfume bottles. Each with a price tag.

"What's the matter?" I asked.

"The matter? I'll tell you what's the matter. The price on the candy is higher than the very best candy in the stores downtown, and they said they were practically *giving* it to the poor working girls. And look at the sign on the perfume: 'Direct from Paris.' It should read: 'Direct from a funnel.' They're not helping the working girl, they're cheating her." She turned stricken eyes on me. "I thought we were doing something charitable for Christmas. Instead, they used us."

Before I could fully understand what all this meant, I felt a heavy hand on my shoulder. I looked up into the stern eyes of a policeman. "So, it's caught up with you, I have," he said.

I had never been this close to a policeman. He towered above me, a handsome red-faced giant with fur earlaps. "Would you be admitting you've been working for the Angels?" he asked.

Odile didn't answer, but I nodded and started to shake. He propelled us into the store. When the Angels saw us their eyes popped big as egg yolks. The policeman marched us up to the counter. He crossed his arms and looked very angry at the Angels. "So you've done it again. Hired children."

The Angels rolled their eyes and wrung their hands.

"'Tis no use pretending innocence," the policeman said. "The little one admitted it." He jerked his head in the direction of the window. "This time it's a ride you'll be taking." I looked and saw the patrol wagon waiting.

The Angels were whimpering. They looked older

than a hundred years. They would go to jail instead of Tennessee. Somehow this was all our fault. Odile must have been thinking the same, for now she blurted. "We didn't get paid. We did it for charity."

The policeman laughed. "Tis a new word for these two."

My voice thawed. "We were doing it for the poor girls," I said.

The policeman's face softened a little as he looked at me.

"And where would these poor girls be?"

I looked hopefully at the Angels, but they were whimpering louder than ever, fluttering their hands helplessly.

Uncle Florival always said Odile could think faster than anyone. She took a step toward the policeman. Then she took a deep breath. "They're not really girls," she blurted. "They're old ladies and they live at the Little Sisters of the Poor, but it makes them feel young to be called girls. There's Mrs. Gates who wears an earphone, Katie Whipple who sings all the time and Clara Schultz who is older than anybody but likes to wear a ribbon in her hair."

"Will you be explaining what that has to do with your being here?" the policeman asked.

Odile took another deep breath. "Every year for Christmas they get hard candy and some oranges and cookies. Maybe stockings and handkerchiefs. I wanted to get them something exciting this year." She looked hard at the Angels. "This year the Angels are going to give each of the old ladies a bottle of perfume. It's in the back room where my sister and I bottled it."

The policeman took off his cap with the ear muffs and he scratched his head. "The Angels *giving?* That I must see with me own eyes."

At that Angelica and Angelina came to life. They ran into the storeroom and came back with their hands filled with perfume bottles. "We'll wrap them in tissue and tie them with red ribbon," they cried.

"Well now," the policeman said, "tis indeed a surprising turn of events." He looked with skepticism at the Angels and then he shrugged. "Who am I to say? Perhaps tis living proof of the Christmas miracle. All the same, I'll be packing the perfume in the wagon and delivering it personally to the home."

When we left, the Angels were busy making fancy packages. They seemed excited about it, and I hoped that next Christmas they would be in their beloved Tennessee.

Christmas morning we always went to five o'clock Mass. As usual, it was cold and dark so early in the morning, but the snow underfoot and the stars on high and the church bells ringing set the scene for the tableau about to unfold. The inside of the church was warm, but dim and shadowy. Then suddenly the all-male choir began *Stille Nacht, Heilige Nacht* soft and low as a whisper, while one by one the candles around the crib were lighted, and then the altar lights. The voices surged louder and louder with the lighting of the candles until all of the church was crowded with music, and I knew once more that this day when Christ was born was the best day of the year.

After church we hurried home to sit around the kitchen table and drink French coffee—coffee with hot milk—and eat warm *streusel* rolls. Then it was time to sit under the tree and open our presents, and I remember that that year I got everything I asked for. Before I had a chance to look at everything a second time, Odile suggested we go by and wish the old ladies at the Home a merry Christmas.

We found them in the dining room, their tables arranged in a circle around a tall tree. But the dining room didn't smell of coffee or food. The scent that greeted us was a mixture of rose and violet and carnation. The old ladies were laughing and dabbing themselves with perfume and when they saw us they cried: "Look what Santa brought."

A little nun smiled as she passed us. "They feel like young girls this morning. Some kind ladies sent them perfume. They also sent boxes of chocolates. We will offer our prayers for their intentions." This, I thought, practically guaranteed that the Angels would be in Tennessee by jasmine time.

We had to hurry away then because all the ladies wanted to daub perfume on us and give us some of their candy and fruit.

On the way home Odile said, "I guess I should have

listened to Papa. He told me that age is not always wise. I put you to a lot of work packing all that candy."

"I don't mind," I said. "Remember Papa also said 'All youth is not ignorant.' It turned out all right."

When we got home there were packages from Aunt Julie and Uncle Louie. They had stopped by while we were at the Home. Odile's present was a blue fan sparkling with brilliants. The card, in Julie's handwriting, read: "They say all the girls at dancing school carry these fans." For once Odile didn't say: "Who are THEY?" She practiced using it, giggling and winking over it coquettishly.

I don't remember a more wonderful Christmas. All day long relatives dropped in and the warm feeling inside me grew and grew. Odile had promised me a warm Christmas glow. I guessed that was what I felt. As for Odile, she went around all day with a smile on her face, as if she were sniffing some delicious fragrance, like rose, or violet, or maybe carnation.

* V *

THE GIVEAWAY PARTY

* * *

For some time now Odile had taken up party giving. To her a party was synonymous with unusual food, entertainment and decorations.

Most of our relatives set what was known as a "plain table"—boiled beef with horseradish, carrots cooked with spareribs, cabbage savory with knack-wurst. Good food, lots of it, but no frills. Odile decided there must be something wrong with these menus since they were not glorified in women's mag-

azines, or to be found among the aspics and chafing
dish recipes in the newspaper's daily cooking column.

Odile had a high regard for the printed word. If the
column had said it was smart to serve dessert first and
soup last, she would have tried it. Aunt Nace said
she read too much and so was being drowned in
American humbug.

When Odile experimented with food, she tried the
results out on the family. "I'm making Candlelight
Salad for supper," she might announce, whereupon
the uncles, if any happened to be around, reached for
their hats. Salad to an Alsacer meant garden lettuce,
salt and pepper, oil poured with the hand of a spend-
thrift and vinegar dispensed like a miser.

The Candlelight Salad turned out to be a banana
standing upright on a round of pineapple, with a min-
iature candle stuck into the tip so it could be brought
lighted into the darkened dining room. It was dramatic, if slightly wax flavored.

Last Halloween Odile had made faces on the
rounded sides of peach halves. The eyes and nose
were cloves and the mouth a gash of red cherry. "Oh
Yerra! It is Nace," Uncle Florival had cried, looking
at his serving. Sure enough it was, the nose straight
and pointed, the mouth thin lipped. "How can I eat
that one?" he had asked in horror.

So it was no great surprise to me that spring day
when Odile called to me from the top of the hen
house. "I'm planning a party. Come on up." I climbed
the ladder set against the grapevines and sat next to

Odile on one of the planks placed across the wire netting.

This was one of our hideaways. Screened by the grapevines and the cherry trees below, which now were in fluffy blossom, if we were quiet no one would know we were here. We could hear the clucking of the chickens below us, and if we stood we could see the vegetable gardens of the neighbors, yet we were invisible to all but the pigeons flying in and out of our dovecot.

Odile waited until I was settled, then she handed me a couple of slices of sugared bread. This was a favorite. Bread, fresh from the oven, spread with sweet butter and sprinkled with granulated sugar. The bread had been baked by Aunt Marthe, who was keeping house for us for a few days. Papa had been sent to St. Louis by the railroad and Mama had gone with him.

"What kind of party you giving?" I asked, biting into a slice.

"A giveaway for Helena."

The news caught me with a mouthful of sugared bread. I swallowed it in one gulp. "You're crazy. Helena wasn't really serious about going to the convent. By now she's probably going to be a movie star again."

"That's what you think," Odile said. "Edie is leaving Monday and Helena is going with her. She's running away."

"Who ever heard of anyone running away to the convent," I said.

Edie was a classmate of Helena's at the Academy. They were "best friends." Edie was entering a convent in Cleveland. Two weeks ago she had asked her friends to a "giveaway" party, at which she had given them her beads, bracelets, lavaliers and odds and ends of jewelry which, obviously, were not proper accessories to coif and veil. After that Helena had talked of nothing but how she would miss Edie. She decided she too would "take the veil." She would go with Edie. The whole thing had been very dramatic. She had taken from her dresser the picture of Herbert, the one of Walter, the snapshot of Don and the one of Clyde. From her walls she had torn her collection of pictures of male movie stars. She had stopped curling her hair and had answered no male telephone calls.

Father Kelmer's eyes had crinkled and he grinned when Mama went to the rectory and spoke to him about it. "Quicksilver to the convent?" It was his favorite nickname for her because she was never still. "She will be in and out. That will make work and trouble. I suggest she change her mind at home. It will be easier for the sisters that way."

When Mama spoke to Sister Bernadette at the Academy she shook her head. "Helena's friend, Edie, has a true vocation, but Helena has 'convent fever.' "

Now I reminded Odile of this.

Odile bent close. "I found her suitcase, all packed, under the bed. I heard her talking to Edie on the telephone. 'I'll go with you if it's the last thing I do.' "

The giveaway party

"I don't believe it," I said.

"At first I thought I'd better send a telegram to Mama and Papa. Then I decided to make sure."

"How?" I asked.

"With a giveaway party."

"You'll invite her girl friends so she can give away her jewelry? You think because Helena likes bracelets and necklaces so much she won't want to give them away, and when she sees she can't make the sacrifice she'll know she hasn't a vocation?"

Odile gave me a superior look. "Who's going to bother giving away jewelry? Think, Shatzie, what is it Helena has that would be the hardest thing to part with?"

I shook my head.

Odile looked at me in triumph. "She'll give away her boy friends."

People were always saying Odile was "different." At times like this I thought maybe they were right.

I wondered just how Odile intended giving away the boys. I looked over her shoulder at the list she was compiling. She was writing down the names of Helena's most loyal admirers; opposite, she listed Helena's best girl friends. "I'll pair them off in some clever way no one ever thought about."

I took another look at Odile's list. Her own name was at the bottom. Opposite she had written: "Paul Reichman."

"Who's he?"

Odile blushed. "Oh, you know, the tall boy with the gold colored hair. He lives up on Navarre Avenue."

"The one who passes here sometimes?"

Odile nodded her head and busied herself with her list.

This handsome bright-haired young man had been passing our house for a couple of weeks. I remembered now that Odile would usually be sitting on the front steps when he went by. If her girl friend, Grace, was with her they would poke each other with their elbows and whisper. He never really looked over but, now that I thought of it, he did walk kind of stiff-legged, as if he thought he were being watched.

Somehow I could not imagine this handsome knight going blocks out of his way to see my sister Odile. He was older, the kind the girls called "classy." Odile, who had just lately, since she started taking dancing lessons, taken to writing in her diary about the boys, was as skinny as ever, her hair fine and unmanageable. I was suspicious. Was she having this party so she could meet Paul Reichman?

"Are you asking Walter Keesling?" I asked.

Walter was a boy Odile's age. The last time he had come over with his folks he had his hair slicked back.

Odile looked down her nose. "Of course not."

"I still think you can't ask a perfect stranger like Paul Reichman."

"He isn't a stranger. Mama knows his mother. They came from the same village in Alsace. His father is in the Turnverein with Uncle Louie. He's a college man, home for the spring holidays. I've already sent him a formal invitation."

"If this is supposed to be a party to give away Helena's beaux, why are you asking Paul? He isn't one."

Odile ignored my question. She stood up. "Now I'll have to talk to Aunt Marthe," she said.

I knew she would have no problem there. Aunt Marthe was a softie. She couldn't say no. At least not to Odile. Besides, she was new to American ways. She was always telling the relatives how smart Odile was. She wouldn't think it at all odd that Odile was planning to give away Helena's beaux, but then Odile would fail to tell her that detail.

It turned out that Marthe was thrilled to be in on the surprise. She helped to conspire. "I see to it that Aunt Lily asks Helena over for the day to take care of the baby. Then she will not see the work going on. Oh Yerra! We have only tomorrow. We must get busy."

This observation proved to be an understatement. When Odile gave a party the house always acquired a personality change. "We'll have to take down all the family pictures," she said. "They're out of style. I read that someplace. And the doilies, we've got to get rid of them. Do you think we'll have time to dye the couch cover?" And so it went. She worked at such a frenzied pace the rest of us were carried along by the sheer excitement of it.

As usual, we were still hard at work when the door-bell rang announcing the first guest. It was amazing to see Odile, who a moment before had been shouting directions like a field marshal, all the while standing on a stepladder fastening the last crepe paper streamer onto the dining-room light fixture, take off her apron and go to greet her guests as if she had a corps of servants in the kitchen. She had read somewhere that the hostess must appear calm and collected even if the house were on fire.

The boys were the first to arrive. Each one came in smiling until he glimpsed a rival. Then he sat down and made a serious study of the roses on the carpet. Here was Herbert who, until two weeks ago, had come to see Helena every Sunday night. Opposite sat Clyde, with whom Helena liked dancing better than anyone. There was Walter who had a sailboat, and Don who took her to all the football and basketball games. Now they sat in opposite corners, like prize fighters, arms folded over their chests, waiting to jump into the ring.

The girls came in a group, a whirlwind of pastel organdies—curly-haired blond Viola, bubbly Hazel, giggly Dorothy, dark-eyed Rosanne. The boys stood for a moment, bowed, then sat down again and re-turned to the roses.

And then Paul Reichman arrived with all his golden blond charm. Wavy hair still wet from the plastering he had obviously given it, eyes blue as the tie he was wearing, and blue serge suit with the new tight fit. I wondered how Odile had been able to snare this knight of the East Side. I took another look at her, as she introduced Paul, to see if she had, while I was not paying attention, outgrown what everyone called her "bony look." But no, her blue organdy dress still looked as if it were shirred around a broom handle.

There were footsteps on the front walk. "Shsh, it's Helena," Odile whispered, and we all ran and hid behind chairs. When Helena came through the door, we leaped at her en masse, screaming: "Surprise."

Helena was not surprised. She was dumbfounded. Here were her recent beaux all lined up in a row, and from the glimmer in their eyes it was apparent each one expected to be the escort of the evening. Helena was not serious about any of them. Going steady was for those ready for marriage. A popular girl might have several interesting boys "on the string." She had to be clever, of course, to keep them dangling contentedly. One rule was to keep them apart. And now here were Helena's admirers not only under one roof but about to be thrown to the girl friends.

I noticed immediately that Helena was wearing jewelry again. Also, her hair was curled. A waterfall of ringlets cascaded down the back of her neck. "She's copying Marguerite Clarke," I thought. So the convent fever had waned, and "Quicksilver" was on the rise. I recognized the jewelry as Aunt Lily's. Helena liked to borrow jewelry.

Odile stood in the center of the room, her hand clapped to her mouth. So she had seen the jewelry and the curls.

Helena uttered little excited squeals, the way girls often do when they meet, and she was elaborate in her greetings to the boys, but it was all with an undertone of "who did this horrible thing to me" and she darted looks at Odile and me. On rare occasions Helena's eyes could look as fiery as my mother's. This was one of the occasions.

Odile darted here and there, trying to pep up the party. She rushed up to me. "Start the phonograph. There's nothing like dancing to break the ice." But apparently that worked only on thin ice. The boys remained glued to their chairs, and the girls huddled together on the couch and giggled about nothing at all.

Paul was an outsider. He, obviously, did not know what the trouble was, but when the record finished he made an effort to save the party. He sat down to the piano and played, by ear, all of the popular ragtime of the day. This at least made the girls happy, and after a while the boys half-heartedly joined them.

Under cover of the music, Helena eventually cornered Odile and me. "Who's responsible for this?" she asked.

"I thought you were going to run away to the convent," Odile said.

"It's a giveaway party," I said. "You're giving your beaux away."

Helena was beyond words for a moment. "March

into the kitchen, both of you," she finally ordered.

I marched, but Odile flew upstairs.

Helena opened the closed French doors into the streamer festooned dining room. "Oh, just wait until Mama comes home," she wailed.

In the kitchen Aunt Marthe was busy making hot chocolate and Uncle Caeser was stacking cups. "Nice party Odile has planned," Marthe beamed. "I tell Caeser, never do I have so much fun; but you, Helena, you should not be in kitchen to see what goes on." Laughingly she turned Helena around and shoved her through the door.

We stood in the dining room looking at the table. Odile had really outdone herself. She had borrowed little Caeser's toy train and had the track running around in a circle. Between each pair of plates she had placed a sign bearing the name of a town between Toledo and Cleveland.

"She's going to pair off the couples by handing out these railroad tickets," I told Helena, getting the tickets from the sideboard and giving them to her. "If a boy's ticket says: 'Destination Fremont,' then he sits with the girl who is bound for the same town. "See, she has Rosanne with Clyde, because she's always been crazy about him, and . . ."

"And where am I?" Helena asked.

"You're up by the train engine. Here, where it says 'All aboard.' Paul Reichman sits between you and Odile."

Helena shook her head. "Do you know, Shatzie, this

could be funny. I almost feel like laughing." Helena's anger never lasted long. She had a heart as sunny as her freckled face. "Poor Odile. She worked so hard. What a job of pairing off she's done. I couldn't have done better myself."

"What are you going to do?" I asked.

Helena sighed. "Tell Odile that Aunt Marthe has the cocoa ready."

Helena went into the parlor. "All aboard," she cried, and she handed out the railroad tickets.

Odile came downstairs very subdued, but the "Oh's" and "Ah's" the girls uttered over the decorations cheered her somewhat.

My role was that of waitress, having been well coached by Odile, who read up on all such things, as to how to set down on the left and take away from the right. What I was putting down was really something. Odile's motif was travel. Sandwiches were rolled to look like train wheels; gelatin salads were replicas of suitcases—how I struggled with carving orange rind into handles. Marthe had baked the cookies. They were best of all. They said "good-by" in every language Odile could handle: *"au revoir— auf wiedersehen—adios—arriverderci."*

"Who's going away?" Paul asked.

"Oh, I am," Helena said lightly. "I'm going to see Edie to the gates of the convent."

There had been a change in the attitude of the boys as soon as she had "given them away" via the railroad tickets, and now that they saw her sitting next to the "college man" they ignored her. They had to turn to someone. Who else but their fellow travelers? So the girls came in for some attention at last.

Paul knew a game called "Let's take a trip," that was just the thing with all the travel decorations. It turned out to be fun and the party became quite gay.

Later, Helena stood on the front porch and said good-by to one couple after another—four boy friends who would never show up on our porch again. I thought it was rather sad.

She came back into the living room and stood there all alone. It was then I heard the soft strains of "Meet me tonight in dreamland." Paul Reichman was at the piano, his hair shining under the rose-fringed parlor lamp, his eyes on Helena. "Room for two," he said moving over on the piano bench. Now I knew why he had been passing the house. The reason was not Odile.

Helena smiled and went toward him. He reached up and laughingly pulled her down next to him. I thought if I were Helena I'd be glad to give up Herbert and Clyde, Walter and Don—four gangling boys —for this smooth and handsome knight.

Odile stood and watched them for a second. Then she sighed and beckoned to me. We closed the French doors and went to work clearing the table. We didn't talk for a while. We were both listening to the music. After a while I saw Odile looking at herself in the buffet mirror. I went and stood beside her and looked at myself. "Shatzie, do you think we'll ever be popular?" Odile asked. I couldn't think of a reassuring answer.

"Well, at least we won't have to send the telegram to Mama and Papa, she said briskly, tackling the table again.

I agreed.

* VI *

TAMING THE BARBARIANS

* * *

Death, to me, was not a dark stranger. It seemed I was born with knowledge of it. Man's life cycle was as plain as that of our clematis vine which sent out green shoots in the spring, purple flowers in the summer, withered in the autumn and died down in the winter.

Funerals sometimes had their advantages. For instance, requiem masses usually coincided with the arithmetic hour at school. I was never good in arithmetic. By being in the choir and singing the Kyrie at funerals, I sometimes got to skip fractions and so escape Sister Mary Matilda's wrath.

When one of our relatives died, we children got to see cousins from all over town, and even from out of town. Aunts and uncles arrived with sad expressions, said words of encouragement to the family, knelt a few moments in solemn-faced prayer, after which the uncles went into the back yard, if it were summertime, or into the cellar, if it happened to be winter, and smoked cigars and talked. The aunts, meanwhile, put on aprons and went to work doing things about the food they had brought. Death was in the parlor with the flowers and the formaldehyde, but in the kitchen there was hot coffee. Too, there was always Aunt Nace, with her head cocked to one side, saying: "Who knows which one of us will be next?" So of course one knew, without anyone explaining, that death, as life, was everywhere.

It was not so easy for Electra Plummer, a girl my age who lived across the street. Electra was being brought up "twentieth century." People in Electra's world did not die. They "passed," and what they passed to was nothing at all. When Electra's grandmother had died a month previous, Electra was not allowed to go to the funeral. She was supposed "to remember her grandmother as she was before she passed." This was civilized, her mother said. Anything else was barbarous.

As a consequence, Electra did not know exactly what happened to her grandmother. It became an obsession with her to find out about this passing business. Since we didn't "pass" in our family, just plain died, Electra was forever trying to get me to talk to her about the dead. At first I didn't mind, there being a kind of excitement in being able to impart my superior knowledge, but I was getting tired of it.

And that is the way I felt the day after Odile's giveaway party. It was the day of the night Mama and Papa were expected home from St. Louis. Electra had invited me over for lunch. "My mother is attending a woman's suffrage meeting," she said.

Electra's mother was very modern. She went in for "movements" and "causes" and she didn't wear pretty dresses as my mother did. She wore tailored suits and shiny sailors and a watch pinned to her lapel. This was considered to be stylish, but to me she looked more like the man of the house.

I didn't like to eat at Electra's because they had a bulldog named Brutus who was allowed indoors at all times. I could smell Brutus as soon as I stepped into the kitchen. No matter what they had to eat, it tasted slightly of Brutus. His bed was under the kitchen sink, along with his bowl of water, but his dog bones might be anywhere.

Electra could cook as well as her mother, that is, she could open cans as well. They were "pals" and so did everything together and that included cooking. I didn't mind the canned food since it was a novelty to me.

Today Electra was emptying a can of tomato soup

into a kettle on the stove. She was a pale, white-haired girl with very prominent veins which made her skin look a little blue. She also had very thin, limp wrists, and she said odd things. Today she said: "I wish I had a mother."

"What do you mean? You've got one."

She turned faded eyes on me. "No, she's my pal. We discuss things. Then I must make all my own decisions. This morning, for instance, we discussed my birthday tomorrow. I have until tonight to decide whether I want my parents to take me to the Museum of Art, or whether I would rather have a dollar."

"You'll take the dollar, of course."

"That's the trouble. If I do, it will look as if I don't want to go with my parents. The three of us are pals in everything, you see. When my father comes home from work, we get dinner together. Then we sing over the dishes."

"I wish we did," I said.

"Oh no," she said. "There is a time to sing and it is not over the dishes. You should sing when you feel like it. Not to pretend you like to do dishes."

She set two soup plates on the table. "I wish my mother would yell at me just once, instead of always reasoning everything out in low tones. I wish we did not go on family vacations all the time and that I could go someplace alone on the train—the way you do to visit cousins sixty miles away. Then it would be fun to come home again. The way we do it, it's no fun to come home because we haven't been apart and we're tired of each other. Only we don't say so. That would not be civilized."

Over the tomato soup, which tasted like Brutus, and the crackers, which tasted like Brutus, we discussed ghosts. "Tell me again about the ghost your mother saw," Electra said.

"It wasn't a ghost. It was a sign."

"Well, tell me about it."

"It was before my little brother died. He wasn't even sick then," I began. "Someone gave my mother a lily plant. It was a warm day and she put it out on the porch to water it. A dog she had never seen before ran up, bit off one of the lilies and dropped it at her feet. My mother knew right away that someone young was going to die. A month later, my little brother got sick. He died in three days. It was sad. Uncle Theofil says the only times funerals are really sad is when children or the very young die."

"Where did your brother go? Tell me again."

"Straight to heaven. Father Kelmer said he didn't have to go to purgatory. He was too young to do wrong."

Electra sighed as she took the dishes to the sink. "Do you know, I think my grandmother would rather be in purgatory than 'passed' into nothing. By the way, someone up on White Street 'passed.' Let's go see who it is."

I wasn't too enthusiastic. Since her grandmother had "passed" Electra wanted to visit every house with a crepe on it. I went along to please her. We would,

if we did not know the family, try to guess the age of
the "passed" by the color and the size of the wreath
on the door. The wreath was also a giveaway as to
whether old Pfalzgraf, the undertaker, had sold the
family a cheap or an expensive funeral.

We would stand in front of the house for a few
minutes, discussing these things, before we would
ascend the porch steps. The door would be opened by
a hand unseen and we would be enveloped by the formaldehyde. This would smart the eyes, so everyone
looked red-eyed and properly sad. We would circle
the coffin solemnly, noting whether it was solid mahogany or one of the cheaper suede ones, and count
the sprays. If a kneeler were provided, we would sink
to our knees under the flickering candles and add our
prayers to the ascending stream of petitions which I
envisioned as a shaft of sunlight reaching to heaven.
Having done what we could to smooth the way of
the departed through the pearly gates, we would
march to the door.

Back on the street Electra would say, "Don't tell
my mother."

As far as that went, I had not told my own mother
of these visits to strange houses, and now we were
headed for another. I knew Electra was looking for
something, but what exactly I didn't know.

When we reached White Street we saw that the
crepe on the door was a large wreath of fresh flowers.
This meant the people either had money or were Irish.
The hand unseen opened the door at our approach, but

this time it had a voice. "Well, and would you now be friends or relatives of the departed, rest her soul."

Right away I knew this was an Irish house, and the Irish being a people I knew very little about, I thought maybe we should turn around and leave, but the voice belonged to a pleasant looking man who I first thought needed a shave, but then I realized he had a goatee. He herded us through a sitting room toward the parlor. The chairs along the wall were filled mostly with black-clad women, all of them talking in whispers. It was then that I heard laughter coming from the back of the house and I was surprised, although no one else seemed to be, the women never stopping in their whispering. Now, in similar circumstances among my relations there would be talking, of course, in the kitchen over the cooking, and maybe even a joke or two, but never loud enough to be heard in the parlor.

The man with the goatee had now led us into the parlor and I was quick to note that the walls and even the ceiling were covered with sprays of flowers, so I knew the departed had either been well liked or had many relatives who had made a good showing. I was just starting to count them—and it seemed a hopeless job—when Electra started crying out loud. The man with the goatee looked surprised. The women stopped whispering. I was dumfounded. This crying of Electra's was something new. We always visited the "passed" with stony faces.

"It's my grandmother," she cried, pointing. I looked to see if this could be so. I had seen her grandmother once, and now I decided there was a resemblance in the way all old people have a way of looking alike, their lives being etched into their faces by their wrinkles.

Electra started crying even louder. The goateed man took her by the hand and led her past the women, whispering again, and into the kitchen. Here there were many people. A round-faced, jolly woman washed Electra's face with cold water, all the while saying: "The poor little darlin'."

I explained that Electra had not been allowed to see her grandmother who had "passed" and so I guessed she had been looking for a dead grandmother and this was the first one she had found.

My Uncle Benedict once told me that the Irish are warmhearted when they are not telling each other how good they are, or when they are not fighting. Today they were not bragging and they were at peace, so they insisted first that we sit in the kitchen and later that we stay for supper. They were drinking something out of small glasses—not red wine like my Alsatian relatives, or beer like my German uncles— but whatever it was they liked it and it seemed to give them comfort.

When Electra asked the man with the goatee if this was a party, he explained that Grandma Kate had had fourteen children, all alive and here today, and forty grandchildren, and she had been in good health, praise be to God, until the moment she breathed her last. The

Lord had saved her from suffering, so it was, in a way, a time of thanksgiving and a time to rejoice for her, even though they would miss her, and yet with the missing of her they knew she was in heaven enjoying her reward, already watching over those left behind, and making sure that they all joined her sooner or later as, God willing, the case might be.

He had a wonderful rolling voice, almost like music, and Electra seemed comforted. "You mean she is a ghost and she is watching us right now?" she asked.

"Well and I think that would be a healing thought now for us, and for you too, to know that our grandmothers are so well situated and getting ready to welcome us, wouldn't you say?"

And come to think of it, it was, and Electra seemed to think so too, because her pale eyes lit up and she smiled.

For supper they had bowls of potato salad, which was a surprise to me, since I thought only Germans could make potato salad. True, they could have done with a good German recipe, but it was good, considering. With it they had all manner of cold meats bought at a store, which again you would never find in the home of one of my relations at a time like this because the women would have been cooking hams all day, but I liked it, having a weakness for bologna.

After supper things got even more interesting because more and more people arrived and some of them came out into the kitchen wiping their eyes, and then

84

THE UNMARRIED SISTERS

taking a little glass of this stuff which was neither beer
nor wine, and Electra and I got to dry the glasses, of
which there were aplenty.

Then Father O'Brien from their church came. All
the people got down on their knees, Electra and I too,
and we prayed for Grandma Kate even though it
seemed she already had a good firm seat up in heaven.

After that I decided we'd better go home since
Mama and Papa would be back on the ten o'clock
train from St. Louis. In parting, the goateed man gave
Electra a big wreath of pink carnations—"In memory
of your grandmother," he said.

It was getting dark when we started home, but still
the twilight was staying on stubbornly the way it does
this time of year, and Electra was hanging onto the
flowers, happy that she knew what had happened to
her grandmother. We had to take a longer way home
because Electra was afraid to carry the wreath past
Dora's house; Dora being a girl with only one parent
and we being a little afraid of girls like that since they
were always bolder, and, who knows, Dora might
even snatch the wreath away.

When we turned the corner into our street, there
stood Mama and Papa, who were home a little early
from their travels it would seem, and with them were
Rosalie and Uncle Benedict. With them too was Electra's mother, still in her tailored suit, and Electra's
father, whose face I never could remember because it
didn't look like anything at all. Everyone was waving
arms and shouting, even Electra's mother, who for

once had forgotten to be low-voiced and reasoning. "Where have you been?" she cried, trying to get the wreath away from Electra.

"We've been to Grandma's wake," Electra said, hanging on, "And I have made my decision about my birthday tomorrow. I want to take this wreath to the cemetery."

Electra's mother gave my mother a look which said: "That is what comes from allowing my child to associate with a barbarian," and she whisked her home, carnations and all, and my mother whisked me into the house and there sat Odile with her chin out and I knew Helena had told about the "giveaway party" last night, a thing Helena rarely did—tell, that is— and Rosalie all the while was talking soothingly to my parents. "The children need their horizons broadened. Ironville and East Toledo are not enough. Odile lives too much in books and imagination. Shatzie is too easily influenced. They need to travel, to see how the rest of the world lives."

Well, I thought, now that I knew how it died, I guess it wouldn't be too bad an idea to see the other side of it. I wondered where we might be going. I heard my father say: "We will see," which was practically an admission that we were going. At the moment I was in no position to ask questions, and probably would not be for a little while, at least not until the carnations in Electra's wreath withered. That would take about two days, I thought.

* VII *

THE GIRL AT THE

BLACKSTONE

* * *

Because of his job as foreman, my father held, for himself and family, yearly passes on the Wheeling and Lake Erie Railroad, which ran from Toledo to far-off West Virginia. Our passes permitted us to board this line at any time we wished. The trouble was that we had no relatives living on the line farther away than Norwalk, a mere sixty miles distant. We couldn't travel beyond that point, for where would we sleep and eat? Only once, on a trip, had we slept anywhere but with relatives. That was the time Papa had a pass

on the "foreign line" called Lehigh Valley, and we had
visited cousins in the Pennsylvania coal country. From
there we had gone to New York, where we stayed in
what might be called a hotel. It was a sort of pension
run by pious nuns bent on protecting innocent travelers from the hinterland, which was any place west
of the Hudson River, against the temptations and
snares of the city.

If any of our relatives went to New York to greet
loved ones on their arrival from the old country, it
went without saying that they sought the protection
of the nuns. No one back home worried if they knew
you were safe at night behind convent walls.

The nun's hostelry had been plain, but fascinating.
For the first time I discovered rooms with numbers
and learned that in a shower bath one got washed from
the top down instead of the bottom up. I learned that
people ate things for breakfast other than coffeecake
or buckwheat pancakes. The nuns had served hashed
brown potatoes, fried eggs and milk. While everyone
knew that eggs were for omelettes and milk was for
heating and pouring into coffee, the hash browns were
an immediate success so far as I was concerned.

We had not had a "foreign line" pass for three years
now. Papa was a most reasonable man. He never asked
for a thing he had not earned. He was a little like a
squirrel gathering acorns for the time of need. When
he thought enough work and time were to his credit,
he would request passes. Not before. But for a month
now, ever since Rosalie had suggested the educa-

tional advantages of traveling for such as Odile and me, my father had looked like a man with a secret that was hard to keep. Then, one Saturday afternoon in early June, he came riding home on his bicycle, his pockets bulging with timetables, a big grin on his face. "It is all arranged," he said. "We take a trip." In those days people didn't "go on vacations." They "took a trip."

A few of the relatives had stopped in, after their weekly shopping on downtown Summit Street, for a cup of coffee and a wedge of *Kugelhopf*. "Oh Yerra!" they cried at my father's announcement, and they looked at one another solemnly, for most of them, once they had crossed the ocean to Toledo, never ventured farther away than Perrysburg, a few miles up the Maumee River.

Papa asked Odile to unroll the large map she had hung on the dining-room wall. Odile was an expert in geography. She knew the map of the United States by heart. Blindfold she could point with accuracy to any state suggested, pinpoint its capital and, without hesitation, give its population, chief industries and climatic conditions. Mama didn't consider this achievement of Odile's so much a talent as a romantic desire always to be where she was not.

As Odile unrolled the big map it slid inch by inch over the wallpaper, which depicted crimson-coated huntsmen riding to spotted hounds while delicate ladies waved handkerchiefs from flowered balconies. The chore finished, Odile sat down next to me. "Gee, if only we had relatives to visit in Chicago," she said. "Then maybe we could find a way to eat fresh figs and Melba dry at the Blackstone Hotel."

Odile was at this time reading a serial running in the newspaper called "The Girl at the Blackstone." The heroine was a member of Chicago's highest society. She was "the beautiful, the spirited, the dauntless Juanita Joyce" who ate figs for breakfast at the Blackstone because she and her love had once done this after an all-night debutante ball. Her love had proposed over the figs. Later they had quarreled—bitterly —and he had gone away. So now, once each month, on the anniversary of this day, Juanita went to the Blackstone to order figs and wait, in the hope he would remember, and so return. Helena too was reading the sad story of Juanita Joyce and the figs. The difference between Odile and Helena was that she was content to have Juanita eat the figs and do the suffering. Odile, as usual, wanted to get into the act herself.

Papa was drawing a circle around Toledo with a purple indelible pencil. We all leaned forward to see on what "foreign line" we would be traveling and where to. As he guided his indelible westward I held my breath. He must be joking. I had always wanted to go out West, but we didn't even have a third cousin west of Fort Wayne.

The purple streak sped on and on. across Indiana, Missouri, Kansas, Colorado, with Nace shrieking an accompaniment of "Oh Yerras" as each state boundary was intersected and passed. When Papa finally drew a purple circle and stopped, Odile was the only one who knew exactly where we were. "The Grand Canyon," she recited. "In the Far West. State of Arizona. The greatest example of erosion and the most sublime spectacle in the world."

Aunt Julie, being new to this country, had never heard of the place. But Aunt Nace had. She rolled her eyes. "Oh Yerra!" she said. "In the moving pictures I see it. Indians ride on horses with no clothes. They burn white men at stakes."

Papa smiled all around. "I have now been with railroad many years. I can ask for long trip pass for my family to go anywhere in country. Man at shop tells me Grand Canyon one fine sight."

Uncle Florival, as usual, took an opposite view. "From pictures I see it strikes me that West is same as desert I see when I am in Foreign Legion. Nothing but sand and camels."

Helena giggled. "No camels, Uncle Florival. But handsome rangers, a girl at the Academy told me."

Aunt Nace remembered another moving picture. "There is no water. Always in moving picture they search for water hole. They find it. It is poisoned. Indians powwow. Steal train. Scalp engineer. Throw train from track. Everybody dies."

Papa looked at Nace with long-suffering patience. "The 'foreign line' called Santa Fe has been running to Far West how many years now? So far not one engineer has lost his hair, or his train." He beamed at Mama and at us children. "We take Pullman."

He might as well have said we were traveling by elephant train. Aunt Nace cried "Oh Yerra!" The relations rolled their eyes, shook their heads and sighed. Uncle Florival pounded the table so hard Mama's hand-painted dishes on the plate rail jiggled. "It strikes me that it is the heat that has affected my own brother-in-law. Who takes Pullman? Only suckers."

Uncle Louie, who had been listening thoughtfully, edged into the conversation. "All of you remember the party for Henry Hockmeier right after sauerkraut stomp when he so foolishly, and without reason, gave up his job here to go out to California. At party was Fritz Flettergold, experienced traveler, who tells us his experiences on trip to Far West. Man on Pullman fell out of top bed. Never is he the same since. Fritz advised Henry to sleep with shoes on. 'Take on train a goose-down pillow. Sleep sitting up. Very comfortable, and besides you are ready for anything at minute's notice.' "

Aunt Julie jerked Louie's sleeve. "We go along with Herman and family to Far West?"

"What you think, I am millionaire?" Louie asked, then went on with more advice from Fritz Flettergold. "He said never eat on diner. Instead, take one bratwurst, two sticks of bologna and plenty of rye bread. Will last all the way to Albuquerque."

It was evident Louie had given considerable thought to the Far West.

Aunt Julie tugged his sleeve again. "We take Pullman. And diner."

Uncle Louie looked at her with love and exaggerated patience. "How do we go? Who gives us passes? Is only my brother-in-law who rides free." He turned back to Papa. "Take Fritz's advice. No Pullman. Much cheaper." It was a well-known fact that Louie, while doing very well, held onto his money.

Papa smiled determinedly. "We go in style. Odile she always wants to see Chicago. We stay one night. From there we take Pullman."

Odile jumped up as if shot out of a cannon. "Chicago," she shrieked, then collapsed into her chair. "Here's our chance," she whispered to me. "We'll sneak over to the Blackstone for breakfast."

I really wasn't interested in Chicago and the famed Blackstone Hotel. Not with the entire West ahead of me. My secret love was a cowboy. He wore a big hat and leather chaps. But Odile held out an inducement. "My treat," she said. "I still have the money Uncle Florival gave me on my name day. Don't you want to know what figs taste like?"

I didn't. But if they were free, what did I have to lose? Besides, it seemed unlikely that we would get away from Mama and Papa long enough to make our debut at the Blackstone.

In the days that followed we packed and unpacked our suitcases, putting in this, taking out that. Helena was busy going to farewell parties, Odile wrote pages in her diary about the coming event and we received advice on all sides. "Take with you postage stamps," Deesie said. "They do not sell them in Far West. And sharp knife, in case rattlesnake bite you." Nace added a chilling note. "Make your will. Who knows?"

Aunt Julie was still trying to get Uncle Louie to go with us. "You promised me a honeymoon when times were good," she reminded him. Her plea looked hopeless until the day we left. We stood in the Union Depot surrounded by piled up suitcases, hatboxes, raincoats, umbrellas, books and lunches, with relatives on all sides handing us going away presents, when Uncle Louie gave in. He said he and Julie would catch up with us in Chicago. "We do not travel dangerously. We sit up all night," he said, but there was a twinkle in his eye.

Since we had no relatives in Chicago, my father had found some nuns for us to stay with, Chicago being another big city where there were temptations and snares. The price of fifty cents per person included breakfast, which I hoped would mean hashed brown potatoes.

It was nighttime when we arrived, and hot. The nuns' hospice was on a side street in the downtown section, and it was almost a replica of the one in New York—varnished, orderly, soundless.

Helena, Odile and I shared a room next to Mama and Papa. Odile and I had a double bed, while Helena had a single in an alcove. We got ready for bed and then Odile pulled up the shade. "Look," she cried.

There, believe it or not, across the sooty rooftops, was the Hotel Blackstone sign. "It's just a couple of blocks away," she said with the awe one might expect if the Taj Mahal suddenly loomed on the horizon. "Oh, it looks so grand. Shatzie, what shall we wear?"

"You're out of your minds," Helena said, and refused Odile's invitation to join us. "I wouldn't have anything to do with such a silly thing." But she did lend Odile her polka-dotted dress with the triple flounce. Our dresses were usually made from the same pattern, with variations according to our ages. Mama had made us traveling dresses of tan Shantung, but Odile did not consider these elegant enough for the occasion. The polka-dotted dresses had been made "for best." Since Helena was the eldest, hers had three flounces, Odile's had but two and I, being the little one, was reduced to one. Odile thought the wearing of Helena's three-flounce dress would add years to her appearance.

Odile's unconscious urge to make everything she wore uniquely Odile sometimes turned out a bit odd. The three of us had leghorn hats with streamers in the back which hung to our shoulders. Now Odile took a length of ribbon from her suitcase and added to the streamers so they reached to the hem of the three-flounce dress. I fell asleep while she was sewing and when I awakened it was the next morning, the sun was in the room and Odile was already combing her hair.

Odile was not considered old enough to wear her

hair in one braid down her back. She was still wearing two looped braids. For this occasion, however, she
had rolled the top of her hair into something which
resembled a fat little field mouse. Having done so
handsomely by the mouse, she had only enough hair
left for a hungry-looking braid to straggle down her
back. She tied a large water silk bow at the nape of her
neck. When she put on her leghorn hat with the
streamers she looked like a walking ribbon counter.

At Odile's insistence I wore her double-flounced
polka dot, and it was immediately evident why Mama
had given me only a single. The double flounce was
extraneous below the knees. Odile assured me that the
extra length made me look "quite old."

Helena awakened while we were dressing. She sat
up for a moment, "You're crazy," she said. "Besides,
you should tell Papa." With that she lay down and
went back to sleep.

When we were ready we slipped out of the room
on tiptoe. All went well until we reached the ground
floor. A nun sat at the desk. She looked at us inquir-
ingly. But Odile could not only rise to an emergency,
she could fly to it. Her face bore an "I'm on my way
to Mass" look as she asked where the chapel was lo-
cated. The nun smiled warmly, said there was no
chapel in the building, but that we would find a church
just a block away. She rose and unlocked the convent
fortress.

Although we had not actually said we were going
to Mass, my conscience started getting troublesome as

we skipped by the open door of the church. This feeling was replaced by one of terror the closer we got to the hotel. I felt as if Nace's Indians were about to powwow around me and burn me at the stake.

Neither Odile nor I had ever been in a real hotel. Every time we passed the Secor in Toledo we would stop and observe it from the outside with the respect due a hotel said to have golden chairs upholstered in velvet, and matching drapery. When we turned the corner and I glimpsed the dark façade of the Blackstone, I stopped. I couldn't do it. Odile took me by the hand. I was the kind of person who would go anywhere if taken by the hand. As we walked up the stone stairs and crossed the lobby my feet never touched solid substance. I wasn't there at all. It was just my spirit that was being swept along, and at the moment the man doing the sweeping was dressed right out of "The Student Prince." He bowed us into the dining room, where a red-coated figure led us to the exact center of the room. Here he was joined by his twin. Simultaneously they shoved us under a table and whisked napkins big as pillow cases onto our laps. From somewhere I got the courage to lift my eyes. We were the only diners in this palace of gleaming silver and dazzling white linen, the size of our carbarn back home. I looked to Odile for reassurance, but she was no longer Odile. By her tragic expression and the lift of her eyebrows I realized that she was now "The Girl at the Blackstone." I was all alone.

Finally Odile acknowledged my presence and, in

what she considered a boarding school accent, said: "I do hope the figs are fresh this morning." I had read enough of "The Girl at the Blackstone" to know this dialogue was straight out of Chapter Five.

One of the red-coats returned to present menus with all the flourish of royal decrees. I took one look. It was in a foreign language. Here was crisis. A situation which I was sure Odile was unprepared for. She gave the menu a glance, there was an instant of puckered eyebrow, then she handed it back with disdain. "We would like figs, if you please, fresh figs, and Melba dry."

The red-coat bowed gravely, his head slightly to one side, his mouth held in tightly. "But of course," he said. "And mademoiselle would like *café en pot noir*, naturally."

"Naturally," Odile said.

When the red-coats returned they carried vast amounts of silver. A domed platter was set before each of us. As if on signal, the domes were removed —with all the pomp of the unveiling of an emperor's jewels—and there before me on a silver doily reposed a regal crown of pale green fig slices.

I am quite sure it was the "Melba dry" that had enticed me into this situation. I thought it a variation of peach Melba, which cost twenty-five cents and which I had never tasted because for that vast sum I could buy five ice-cream sodas. The prospect of a peach Melba free had been too much for me to ignore. But now I discovered that this Melba was cold and skinny toast filed neatly into a silver rack.

Every time I looked up, the red-coats were watching, so I put a slice of fig into my mouth. Horrors! It tasted a little like a dandelion stem, but more like a petunia leaf. Quickly I put my napkin to my mouth, looking to Odile for help. She observed me icily. I swallowed the fig, then rammed Melba dry into my mouth to kill the taste. I took a swallow of *café noir* and shuddered.

I looked over at Odile to see how she was faring. With boredom, deliberation and great poise, she was eating slice after slice, but with every mouthful she seemed to get whiter. I knew Odile's tricky stomach and it worried me. But now she beheld me calmly. "Figs take getting used to. Try some more."

Dutifully I tried another slice. Alas, I came to the conclusion then and there that the Good Lord might have made the fig tree so the leaves could be used as raiment, as it says in the Bible, but he surely never intended the fruit to be eaten—at least not at the Blackstone, by me, with royalty in strict attendance.

When Odile was presented the bill, I thought the figs had finally gotten her. When the red-coats were busy elsewhere she whispered, "How much money have you?"

"A dollar and thirty cents, in change," I whispered.

By the time one of the red-coats returned, the breakfast bill was now stacked with Odile's two dollar bills, which she had figured would more than cover the breakfast, plus my four quarters, two dimes, one nickel and five pennies.

The red-coat counted it out and left a nickel and five pennies on the plate. Odile eyed him with cool condescension, then she airily shoved the change in his direction, gathered up her crochet bag and, while the royal red-coats sprang forward somewhat over-gallantly to pull us out from under the table, she said: "The figs could have been just a little sweeter, don't you think, Shatzie? I do believe the season is ending." To all of which I was quite willing to agree.

We sauntered boredly from the still empty dining room and out of the hotel. Once on the street, Odile took my hand. "We'd better run."

When we passed the church we ducked in. Odile was the soul of honor. She had intimated we were going to church, so to church we would go. Mass was about over. We bowed to a saint or two and came out.

"What good did it do—going to the hotel," I asked Odile on the way back to the nuns.

Odile's eyes glowed. "Now I know what it's like to eat figs at the Blackstone," she said.

"But we spent all our money."

"I'll never forget it," Odile said. "If I live to be a hundred, I'll always remember it. What an 'experience.'"

We started running, and again I noticed how pale Odile looked. "I hope the nuns have hashed brown potatoes for breakfast," I said, and at that a shudder ran through Odile's skinny polka-dotted frame.

Papa met us at the entrance. "Good girls you are to go to church while on vacation, but you must always tell your Mama and Papa first. What is wrong Odile? You are not feeling well?" He reached into his pocket for a peppermint, but Odile grasped her throat and ran up the stairs.

"What makes Odile sick?" Papa asked me later in the dining room.

"You know how tricky her stomach is," I evaded. "All this odd food she's been eating on the trip."

Mama came into the dining room then and said the nuns had made a pot of green tea for Odile and she was feeling better.

Helena came down, late as usual, and reported that Odile couldn't be very sick because she was busy writing in her diary.

"Now what could she be writing about so soon this morning?" Papa asked.

"You know Odile," Helena said. "She's probably had an 'experience.' "

The nuns did serve hash browns and, as I began eating them with great appetite, I was glad I had been satisfied just to taste the figs. I wasn't like Odile. I didn't have to know how it was to eat a whole dish of them. I didn't have to know everything firsthand. It was sometimes enough just to have people tell me about things.

* VIII *

CONSIDER THE LILIES

*　*　*

Uncle Louis need not have worried about the quality
of the meals cooked by the chef aboard the Atcheson,
Topeka and Santa Fe. Since the Houck family rode
"deadhead" we were not privileged to board the
line's haughty flyers. Besides, our train must yield the
track to them at the most unlikely places. It carried no
diner and we were to eat our meals with Mr. Fred
Harvey, whoever he might be.

　　We soon discovered that being "side-tracked" often

gave us the added adventure of exploring a bit of America unheralded in glowing travel brochures. Odile gathered such fascinating bits as this to record in her diary:

> "Side-tracked at EXCELSIOR. Population 2500; one bank; one drugstore; two churches; principal industry, the fattening of hogs. Elmer Hotchkiss, mayor. Mrs. Hotchkiss winner of the annual preserving contest. Twelve bottles of her Sunshine Cherries on display in the Hotchkiss Drug Store window, along with the tatted pillow slips she won as her prize. Aunt Julie spent so much time trying to figure out the tatting stitch, we almost missed the train's departure."

Odile also recorded the fauna and flora she observed from our train window. Sometimes she became poetic.

> "The fields of the Great Middle West stretch to the horizon like soft green blankets on which lazy brown cows lie down to chew their cud and think their bovine thoughts."

Once introduced to Mr. Fred Harvey's system of dining, which meant getting off the train three times each day and eating en masse in a depot dining room, we found it had advantages. For the flat price of one dollar we could order all items listed on the menu.

The only obstacle in the path of the dedicated diner was the lack of time. It wasn't possible to devour, say, a breakfast steak, plus a slab of ham, plus a brace of broiled trout, in twenty minutes. But no one could say we didn't make the effort.

The Harvey System also provided a good opportunity to size up the other passengers. They did a little sizing up too. After the first meal stop, three boys were vying to sit on the observation platform with Helena.

As we traveled westward, Odile's diary took on a romantic flavor: "We are now in the land of the cowboy, the juniper tree and the ten-gallon hat. Here men are men, and a cowboy and his horse are never parted."

As we passed greasewood, sagebrush and table mountains, Odile and I had long conversations on the merits of western men. We agreed that a man with a sun-browned face and clear blue eyes, a man who wore a ten-gallon hat, chaps, and who sat his pinto pony as if he had been born there, was definitely to be trusted, and was certainly more desirable than a pale-faced easterner with an office-chair slump. I personally doubted that such a man as our dreamy westerner existed outside the movies, so it was somewhat of a surprise to meet him almost immediately after our arrival at the Grand Canyon.

While still on the train, Odile had copied into her diary, from a travel brochure: "The canyon is a mile deep and seventeen miles wide. Here you can see the very inside of the earth as if you'd cut into a giant layer cake."

Seeing twelve layers of Grand Canyon Cake and the cowboy on his pinto pony at one and the same time completely shattered both Odile and me, and subsequently caused us to endanger life and limb.

It had previously been agreed that we would see the canyon sensibly, from the rim. Even Odile had thought this wise. She was not only afraid of high places, she had a distrust of anything that walked on four feet with the exception of cats. To descend the trail to the Colorado one rode a mule. Aboard the train we had heard many wild stories—of mules losing their footing, of mountain slides, of travelers never heard from again. So it had been agreed, all around, that we would view the canyon cake from the safe distance of its frosting.

But that was before we met the cowboy—that great guide and swaggering trail blazer, Arizona Jack.

We were at the canyon rim for our first look, with everyone pointing and exclaiming, and Uncle Louie taking pictures, and Mama crying, "Oh Yerra, I did not believe it would be so big," and Papa saying, "Look, children, you see here what the inside of the earth looks like the whole world over."

Just then, coming up from the trail that went down to the Colorado River, we saw the mule train, headed by the guide in ten-gallon hat and leather chaps. He sat a pinto pony and led his string of riders so close to us we all backed up a bit. I saw that his eyes were indeed blue and his face well tanned. He not only sat his pinto as if he'd been born in the saddle, but as if he had ridden it in one or two previous existences. As he came abreast of us, his level blue eyes engaged us frankly and he grinned, showing straight white teeth. Our gaze followed him as he, straight backed, led his train toward the corral. I noted, however, that the members of the train sat their mules with something less than the bravado of the leader. One fat man seemed actually to be bent over double.

As they rode into the corral, Odile read aloud the sign over the gate: "Arrange for your trail trip to the floor of the canyon at the lodge office."

She caught my eye. I knew immediately that she was planning something. I looked away quickly. And then the cowboy and the pinto were back. Again he rode close to us. This time he took off his ten-gallon hat and saluted in a wide, sweeping gesture. "Howdy," he said, in deep canyon tones. Then he rode off into the sunset.

"Oh Yerra! A real live cowboy," Aunt Julie said.

"A very friendly fellow," Papa said. "I should have offered him a cigar."

"Perhaps we see him again," Louie said.

"I think it's important that we do," Odile said. "Now that we're here, I'm convinced that we'll have to go to the bottom of the canyon if we're to know what it's really like."

This was a complete reversal from her previous convictions. Everyone looked at her in surprise. Excepting Helena. She was still looking after the retreating horseman. "I wouldn't go down if they paid me," she said with finality.

Uncle Louie, who was nervous just standing at the rim, broke in quickly. "We see plenty from here."

Odile's gaze met mine across the clear Arizona air. "Shatzie and I want to go down," she said.

I realized with terror that my exchange of confidences with Odile regarding our preference for western men was about to drag me down miles of rugged canyon trail, unless God or chance intervened.

It was Papa who came to the rescue. "Foolish talk. You cannot go alone. That is sure."

Julie, who was absolutely ecstatic over the canyon, broke in, "Louis and I will be glad to ride with the children."

Good-looking, strong Uncle Louie, who was always so sure of himself, paled as he listened to Julie's offer. Technically, they were on their honeymoon. Any show of fear was then unseemly and unromantic. He sat down limply on a boulder. "I say it is foolish. We see all that is necessary from the top."

"But I want to see it from the bottom up," Julie coaxed. She was not really brave about riding a mule, but she loved this America and she wanted to become acquainted with every pebble of it.

The prospect of riding a mule was blood-chilling to me. I had once sat atop the broad high back of a plow horse on a cousin's farm in Norwalk. This simply because someone had teasingly put me there.

The horse had promptly plodded to his stall in the barn, a distance of some hundred feet. I had remained shaken for days.

As for Odile, she had even less riding experience, a situation which I was afraid was being overridden in her logical mind by the fact that opportunity knocks but once.

Helena wrinkled her nose. "You can all go. I'll sit on the veranda and read."

Mama, who never got within ten feet of a farm animal if she could help it, took refuge behind Helena's tender age. "I could not leave her alone," she said.

Papa never boasted of male superiority in matters of bravery, yet it never could be said that he was a coward. He usually was able to reason his way out of an uncomfortable situation. Today was no exception. "We have no riding clothes," he said. "You saw the riders. They wore khaki pants. Even the women."

Papa's sane observation gave everyone a transfusion of courage. With the exception of Helena and Mama, we were now all lovers of the mount.

"One fine trip it would have been," Uncle Louie said, his self-assurance back. He took a deep breath. "I would have been the first to say we should not miss such a trip had we the proper clothes."

My blood ran warm and adventurous again. "Aw gee," I lied, "I was looking forward to it."

Papa smiled and nodded sympathetically. "I too would have gone. After all, I could not allow my little girls to go without me." He patted Odile on the head. "Come now we have good dinner. Tomorrow we hire limousine and we ride around rim of canyon."

As we entered the lodge, it was Odile who first saw the sign hanging over an alcove along the back wall. It read: "RENT YOUR TRAIL CLOTHES FROM SAGEBRUSH SAM."

The enemy we had dispersed at our rear was now in frontal attack, aided and abetted by Odile. How a minority of one could carry along a reluctant majority was difficult to understand, but here we were at the counter presided over by plaid shirted, bowlegged, wizened Sagebrush Sam.

"Surely he cannot outfit all of us," Uncle Louie said.

But he could.

Papa and Uncle Louie looked at each other in dismay. "We have never been on a mule," Papa said. "It would not be wise for so many to go down together who do not know how to ride, is that not true?"

Sagebrush Sam rolled a cigarette. "Pardner, even a week-old baby could ride that thar trail. The mules know the way. All you do is sit and enjoy the scenery. Pretend you're in your old rocking chair back home on the back porch."

Within five minutes every one of us, with the exception of Mama and Helena, was measured, weighed and signed up for the pack trip.

"The mules'll be agitting along on this little walk o' their's at nine in the morning," Sagebrush said.

"How long does the trip take?" Uncle Louie asked.

"Why you all will be back here at five o'clock in the evening. Not a minute later."

Uncle Louie counted the hours. "Oh Yerra! Eight hours we sit on mule. Oh Yerra!"

At eight-thirty the next morning we were back to claim our trail clothes. I, personally, had prayed that the mules would have developed carbuncles during the night and so would be indisposed. But Sagebrush Sam was whistling cheerfully as we approached. "Women and children first," he cried, handing out clothes. He did indeed have pants and shirts and puttees to fit each of us. He had them by the simple expedient of taking all sizes off the same pile.

We must have emerged from the lodge a fine sight indeed. Odile's pants turned out to be a little large of seat and the shirt droopy of shoulders. Her straw sombrero fell to her eyebrows.

Aunt Julie, on the other hand, looked quite elegant for one about to hit the western trail. Her pants fit her very well indeed, and the shirt likewise. Julie had a lovely sapphire necklace and drop earrings to match. Uncle Louie had bought them for her in Paris. These she had been reluctant to entrust to anyone. She had intended hiding them in her blouse, but once she got into it, there was no room for the sapphires, so she wore them. They gave her the air of a *femme fatale* I had once seen in a spy moving picture. The *femme fatale* had insisted on wearing her diamonds on all dangerous assignments. "To give me courage," she had cried in one scene. In the last shot she was in front of the firing squad. She went down, diamonds blazing. The memory of the picture now struck an ominous note. If I was scared before, Aunt Julie's sapphires practically put me into a state of shock. I had a mental picture of her, broken and crushed, at the bottom of the canyon, her sapphires glittering in the desert sun.

Since we had left the bulk of our luggage at Williams on the main line, and since we had intended just riding around the rim of the canyon, none of us had brought sturdy shoes. They were the one item Sagebrush Sam could not supply. Aunt Julie had only flimsy high heeled pumps. Odile and I had on our best vanilla colored sandals. The high heels and the vanilla gave a sort of stylish air to our western garb. I could very well do with this extra touch of sophistication. My knickers, supposed to reach just below the knee, fell to my ankles, so that my buttoned puttees had a somewhat lumpy fit. There was too much shirt to stuff into the pants, so it hung about me like a pup tent. When I put on my sombrero I became at once the headless horseman.

In contrast to the finery of the ladies, Uncle Louie looked like a worn-out prospector in his faded tans. Papa, being long-legged, found that his trousers reached only to mid-calf. When he mounted the mule he towered above the beast, making it appear so sad and put upon it seemed indeed an imposition for Papa to burden him.

I am quite certain that the Grand Canyon Trail

Service never before or since handled such a string of mass incompetence on one trip. Just getting us into the saddles was a major achievement. When we were all in place, the corral roustabouts heaved a sigh of relief which must have echoed around the canyon.

It was at this point that the cowboy on the pinto pony made his entrance. He approached slowly through the corral gate and surveyed each and every one of us like a general inspecting troops. He was indeed as handsome, tanned and clear-eyed as I had remembered from last night. His blue silk neckerchief matched his eyes.

When he came abreast of Odile and me, he grinned. "I thought there were three of you girls," he said.

For once Odile was tongue-tied, but I found my voice. "My older sister said she wouldn't go on the trip if you paid her. She'd rather sit on the veranda and read."

Arizona Jack grinned and gave us places directly behind him.

We were just ready to leave when the pack train was held up for one last rider. It turned out to be a red-haired girl with a southern accent. She seemed about sixteen and her name was Lucy Mae. Once mounted, she rode to the head of the train, crinkled her eyes at Arizona Jack and said: "Ah think ah'd better ride close to you, mister, 'cause ah don't know anything atall 'bout animals lak these heah mules."

I thought, here is where Odile loses her place behind Arizona Jack, but when we left the corral, a pouting

Lucy Mae brought up the rear. Odile turned around, gave me a salute of victory and we were on our way.

Well now, this is going to be easy, I thought. True, the "rocking chair" was a bit bumpy under me, but as we rode out of the corral I copied Odile and sat my mount with what I thought was a casual air. Arizona Jack took us right past the lodge and there sat Mama and Helena with her book. Arizona stopped our caravan long enough for Mama, from a distance, to tell us to be careful, and for Helena to take a snapshot of all of us, including Arizona and his pinto. Then we all waved bravely and we were off.

Abruptly we passed the lodge and rounded a curve. We were faced with the canyon ruggedly layering to the Colorado and the trail was a narrow shelf hanging over nothing. It was the first time I appreciated how smart my sister Helena was. I thought of her sitting placidly on the lodge veranda reading while I was committed to ride this corkscrew trail to the Colorado. My stomach was already down there waiting. It had plummeted five thousand feet straight down when I realized my mule, whose name was Lillian, would not remain on a horizontal plane, but would make the trip perched at a forty-five degree angle, her rump sticking up behind me, and her ears to the ground, with me somewhere in between clutching all the leather I could lay hands on.

The moment we left civilization behind, Lillian took control of me, the trail, in fact of the canyon. After the first spine-melting hairpin turn, she swiveled her head around and looked me full in the face and her expression plainly said: "You asked for it." Thereafter she stopped at will, and with great leisure, whenever she felt the urge to nibble at some choice bit of vegetation along the side. Then she would go at a paralyzing gallop to catch up with Gloria, the mule Odile was riding.

As we descended ever lower and lower, all visible mule goodies disappeared from the trail and I felt easier, but not for long. Lillian's sixth sense detected nourishment along the steep sides of the canyon which she could reach by clinging to the trail with one hoof, the other three, plus me, hanging over the edge of the trail, poised high above the Colorado.

"Let's get off and walk back," I said to Odile, when she turned in the saddle to look at me. Odile smiled calmly and patted Gloria's rump. But I saw how stiff her back was and how she clutched the reins. Odile was scared, but Odile was "in character." When Arizona Jack turned back to look at us, she saluted him as one expert horseman to another, yet I knew it had been a major effort to unglue her fingers from the reins.

I wondered if Odile's rented khakis were rubbing her skin as mine were in the "rocking chair" descent. It wasn't hot. It was boiling. I didn't dare turn to see how Papa, Aunt Julie and Louie were faring. I didn't dare even look at the canyon. I was too busy praying and helping Lillian find her foothold with each step. I asked myself, was it worth it? Was Arizona Jack's back broad enough, his eyes blue enough and his grin wide enough? No, I decided. Odile could have him. All to herself.

Not quite. There was Lucy Mae who was indeed as helpless as Odile was efficient. "Oh Mistah Arizona Jack, somethin' is sure enough wrong with these heah stirrups," she cooed, whereupon Arizona dismounted, squeezed between the mules and the canyon wall, to attend to the stirrups. It wasn't long before her reins were "terribly fouled up Mistah Arizona Jack." Again we rested our mules while Arizona proceeded to the rear of the pack train. Odile turned around in her saddle. She lifted her eyebrows in great disgust. "Tenderfoot!" she said.

It was evident to me, even in my petrified state, that battle lines were forming between the helpless Lucy Mae and my efficient sister.

Halfway down the canyon, at a wide spot along the trail, Arizona called for a rest period.

When I tried to get off Lillian my legs refused to straighten out and I fell flat on my face. As I lifted my head, I saw Odile dismount. She was wincing and the perspiration made pathways down her dusty face, but she smiled and swaggered as if a ride along the "devil's corkscrew" was a thing she did every day. I thought it must be killing her to walk upright, but she did it.

Louie, meanwhile, crawled on hands and knees and lay down in a shady spot as if to die. Needless to say, Lucy Mae had to be lifted off her mule by Arizona Jack. Papa managed to stagger off his mount and help

Aunt Julie who, along with her sapphires, was a bit dusty. Odile helped Arizona Jack administer canteens of water to the stricken. When Lucy Mae recovered a little, she pulled a compact from her hip pocket, adjusted her curls and powdered her dusty nose. Odile's eyes met those of the amused Arizona. Her superior smile seemed to say, "You and I, we are real westerners. The others!!!"

After a while Arizona started explaining the formations of the rock about us. "What you see here is a cross section of the earth's crust."

In the realm of statistics no one excelled Odile. "There are twelve major layers," she said learnedly.

Arizona acknowledged her contribution. "Each layer represents a different age," he said.

Odile touched the rock wall at her back. "This is trilobites," she said importantly.

Arizona looked at Odile with admiration. "I've never known a tourist to have so much information about the canyon," he said.

The tribute went to Odile's head. For the balance of the rest period she talked to Arizona about red flood-plain deposits, dune sands and the mystery of the Colorado River. I was proud of her. Odile's knowledge, like the canyon, was bottomless. The rest of us listened in awe. Excepting Lucy Mae. Her soft white features were drawn down in a pout.

Back in our saddles we came to a particularly steep section of trail. Arizona told us to dismount, take hold of the bridle and lead our mules down the treacherous incline. Halfway down Lucy Mae cried, "Oh Mistah Jack, Daphne's gone."

Sure enough, Lucy Mae's mule was missing. We saw her high up on the trail headed for the rim and her old corral. Unlike Odile and me, to say nothing of Lucy Mae, Daphne was immune to Arizona's charm. She answered his honeyed coaxing with an indifferent swish of her tail. Arizona started up after her on his pinto. He couldn't pass her on the narrow trail and she kept ahead, occasionally sending him a coy look over her shoulder. It was not until Arizona was able to get ahead of her by crossing an arroyo that he could herd her back down to finish her eight-hour day.

"How can that Lucy Mae be so stupid," Odile said to me, a comment which was highly debatable since Arizona now asked Odile to exchange places with Lucy Mae. "You are so efficient," he said. "Lucy Mae better ride behind me, while you bring up the rear."

As the two girls exchanged positions, Lucy Mae smiled sweetly. "Ah wish ah was as smaht as you," she said. I realized then and there that maybe Lucy Mae was only a couple of years older than Odile, and her head was filled with nothing more substantial than Arizona dust, yet her shrewd maneuvering had gotten her exactly where she wanted to be, while Odile and her brains were bringing up the rear.

But once we reached the Colorado it was Odile's turn to have the place in the sun. We were spread along the brown satin river, eating from box lunches.

It was cool and pleasant and the food made us forget our aches. Even Papa and Uncle Louie took on life again, and Aunt Julie asked questions about the different colored rock.

Arizona Jack explained how the canyon had been under water again and again, and each time the river had left a different colored layer of mud.

"It's like a calendar," Odile interrupted enthusiastically. "A calendar of the past millions of years."

While Arizona Jack might be able to supply enough information to satisfy the ordinary tourist, Odile, with her usual methodical approach, had learned the canyon's history back to the stone age. Arizona Jack closed his eyes and let Odile take over.

Lucy Mae lazily threw a pebble into the Colorado. "Well, I declare," she said. "If we haven't got the National Geographic right here with us."

I saw Papa give Odile a queer look and I remembered his once saying that knowledge's true use is to develop and cultivate mentally and morally. Odile was using it to show off. To get a man's interest.

I heard Uncle Louie whisper to Julie. "Which of the two gets the cowboy?"

Aunt Julie shrugged. "Neither."

So I was surprised, just before we got back into the saddle for the return ride, to hear Arizona say to Odile: "We have a mighty interesting program tonight. You must all come. There'll be dancing."

He swung into his saddle, blue eyes level, back straight, while Odile gave me a flushed and triumphant look. I had seen and heard, but somehow I couldn't believe.

Halfway up I buckled and practically lay down on Lillian, but Odile was a marvel. She sat her mule as straight as Arizona sat his pinto. She even managed to sing "Home on the Range" and brought a little life to the wilting pilgrimage. She was truly a girl of the West, I thought. She could keep up with the man of her dreams and show him she could take it.

It was exactly five o'clock when we emerged at the top of the trail. Lucy Mae had to be lifted off Daphne, of course. She did look pale. We all did, as we hobbled over to the lodge. Excepting Odile, of course. She walked with vigor and bounce as if she could immediately make another round trip to the Colorado with pleasure.

When we reached our room, Helena, cool and fragrant in a white linen dress, was putting a red ribbon around her dark hair. "Have a good time?" she asked.

"Oh, wonderful," Odile cried and collapsed on the floor.

Helena started pulling off Odile's puttees and her sandals. "Call Mama," she ordered.

Mama came running. "What is wrong?"

"I'm dying," Odile wailed. "Oh, I ache all over. Don't touch me. Oh! Oh! Oh!"

Mama prescribed a warm bath for both of us.

Inspection showed that we were covered with blisters from our rocking chair ride. Odile was much worse than I. Mama lathered us with salve, then rolled us in cool sheets. We couldn't go down to dinner. Helena brought us iced tea and toast.

The Arizona sun went down in brassy splendor and purple shadows spread over the canyon. Soon it was a dark velvet night embroidered in brilliants, the air heady with romance. In our medicated sheets, Odile and I sat at the open window and watched the tourists below as they promenaded under the archways, examining Indian pottery and beadwork. A way off there was music, and laughter floated on the soft night. I saw Helena in her white dress and pointed her out to Odile. She was with a group of young people, and who was standing right beside her? Arizona Jack— romantic as the night itself in fancy white satin shirt and bright neckerchief. He was looking down at Helena, listening intently to what she was saying. I would have been quite willing to bet that Helena was at that moment not quoting canyon statistics.

A line from the bible nagged at me: "Consider the lilies of the field"—a strange thing to consider here on the Arizona desert, next to a rock formation millions of years old, where, I am sure, lilies never bloomed.

* IX *

THE DEVIL LIVES IN

CALIFORNIA

* * *

Papa loved to tell good news. How he was able to
keep from us the fact that our passes had been extended to include California, I'll never know. I imagine my mother, who was of the opinion that antici-
pation subtracted from the sum of realization, had
something to do with this. It all happened because
when Uncle Louie decided to take Aunt Julie on the
trip, he found he could very well combine business
with their belated honeymoon if he continued on to
the Coast. When Mr. von Hoffner, Papa's boss, heard

of this, he immediately saw to it that Papa's passes included the California trip. This was a tribute to Papa's years of loyal service. It was also a tribute to Papa's ability to smooth the ruffled feelings of Hungarian, Pole, German, Alsatian, Bohemian or Swiss. The workmen didn't always see eye to eye with the railroad, but they trusted "Mr. A Number One Houck."

It was not until the moment Odile and I were at our lowest ebb, practically at death's door from our descent, via ornery mule, to the bottom of the Grand Canyon, that Papa produced the passes.

A good part of our anguish must have been mental, for our blisters faded into insignificance and the cowboy on the pinto did likewise at the fabulous news. Odile immediately became so enmeshed in plans for our entrance into glittering movieland that she forgot to moan and groan.

Helena had been movie struck for a long time. At home her bedroom walls were covered with photographs of Warren Kerrigan, Creighton Hale, William S. Hart and Carlyle Blackwell. Especially Carlyle Blackwell. In movieland she would not be apt to do as she had at the canyon—sit out the time reading. She was so pretty—everyone said she looked like Mabel Normand and that she should be in the movies —I was convinced if a director saw her, she would become a star overnight.

As for me, my deep and well kept secret was that

I would grow up to be beautiful and marry James Cruze, star of the serial "The Million Dollar Mystery."

Odile had no movie idols. Writing a fan letter, or tacking a movie star's picture on her bedroom wall, would never have occurred to her. She was, however, interested in film plots. After seeing the latest episode of a Pearl White serial, she would complain: "The story was stupid. Now if they had used one of mine . . ." It was a fact that Odile wrote one movie scenario after another. Using the pen name of Velda Vaine she bombarded Selig, Vitagraph, Essanay, Griffith and Kalem with her literary missiles. They shot them back with lightning speed, usually unopened.

Now, buoyed up by her impending invasion of movieland, she bought several large tablets at the canyon trading post, and once we were back on the mainline train she spent most of her time outlining a new scenario the title of which was: "The Clock Strikes Twelve." Her heroine was Lady Naysmith, American-born wife of Lord Naysmith who was being held captive in a castle on the Thames. Lady Naysmith, who was not accepted by the lord's family, had until twelve midnight to save her titled husband from being cast into the Thames with a stone about his neck, and thus endear herself forever to her repentant in-laws. As Big Ben toned hour after hour, suspense mounted. At the first stroke of twelve it was practically unbearable. At least Odile said it would be when she was finished with it.

The fact that Odile had never been to England, knew no titled persons and in truth did not know whether Big Ben could be heard on the Thames, did not deter her. She stopped writing just long enough to eat at the Harvey Houses and to send post cards.

No one we knew back in Toledo had ever been to California, so we bought post cards by the dozen and bragged to even remote acquaintances that we were California bound, to pick oranges right off the trees and to see movie stars. Odile went even farther. She wrote that she expected to visit one of the studios.

How to get to see the movie stars was an important topic of conversation as we neared Los Angeles. "I think I'll just stand outside of Kalem and wait for Carlyle Blackwell to drive through the gates in his Locomobile," Helena said.

Papa, who had been listening, leaned across the aisle. "We take touring car called rubberneck. Henry Hockmaier tells me one sees everything that way. I am sure it passes moving picture studios."

"I don't want to just go past a studio," Odile said. "I want to go inside."

Papa shook his head. "Impossible. Even Henry has not been in studio."

Henry Hockmaier, the sausagemaker, was our one acquaintance in California. Everyone back home had been shocked when Henry, who was doing very well supervising the making of German sausages, tired of Toledo. It happened without warning right after the sauerkraut stomp, and I remembered how Cousin Gustave's daughter, Celie, had had red eyes for a week after Henry left.

In Toledo Henry had been well paid for his skill and he had saved his money. This he had invested in a shop of his own on the outskirts of Los Angeles. He had now been in California the better part of a year. We considered him an authority on life in the West.

Papa had not known in advance that we would go to California, so he had not lined up any nuns out there who looked after the well-being and safety of tourists. This was serious. The reputation of Los Angeles and the nearby moving picture studios had reached us in Toledo through an indisputable source, almost first hand, you might say. We had friends in the Irish parish who were friends of a Mrs. O'Callahan who was a friend of the mother of movie idols Tom and Owen Moore. Tom and Owen were probably Toledo's best-known celebrities, but their mother was reported to consider movieland the abyss of sin. "May the saints protect and preserve you," she was quoted as telling any young girl who aspired to being a movie star.

While the information was strictly hearsay, Nace was sure it was true. "They say California is paradise so, naturally, the devil makes his home there," she had said often enough.

So it would seem California was a place where we surely would miss the protection of the nuns. Papa did the next best thing. He put the safety of his family into the hands of Henry Hockmaier.

I knew Henry mostly from the butcher shop. Whenever we crossed the Cherry Street bridge to shop on downtown Summit Street, our last stop would be Henry's for a length of smoked Munchen to cook with carrots and potatoes, or a few yards of knackwurst to flavor the sauerkraut. Henry's section of the shop never smelled of aging meat, but of clean sawdust which covered the floor, spices and freshly grated horseradish which stung the eyes. Usually he would be humming "Halli, Hallo." If he wasn't humming or whistling it, he was playing it on his gramophone, which stood at the back of the shop.

He had called on us occasionally on Sundays after Mass, wearing a stiff black suit which smelled of mothballs. So I had a mental picture of Henry meeting us in Los Angeles wearing the same stiff suit, which Papa said he had brought from Germany, and at first I did not recognize the man coming toward us in the Los Angeles depot with arms spread in welcome. He did not have the big mustache, and his face was sun-tanned and he wore a natty looking blue serge coat, white serge trousers and Panama hat. It was not until he cried: "Halli, Hallo, it's the Houcks," that I recognized him. His arms were as the protecting wings of an angel. Right away it was obvious we did not need the nuns. Henry had arranged for everything. He had rented an apartment for us, by the day, "Near my shop," he said. "Room there is for all of you. Cheaper than hotel it is."

We ate at a German restaurant and then Henry

loaded us and our baggage onto an electric car. It was almost dark when we reached the apartment, a mass of pink stucco decorated with bluebirds, called "Al's and Alice's Wonderland." Adorning the lawn were painted cement figures of the Cheshire cat and the dormouse.

Henry pointed proudly to his sausage shop directly across the street. It was shaped like a wienerwurst and was wedged in between a windmill, which turned out to be a bakery, and a toadstool which sold malted milks.

We entered Al and Alice's Wonderland through a looking glass door. We were squeezed into a midget elevator, along with our luggage, before we realized it was self-service. We had never even heard of such a thing and we clung together in terror as Henry manipulated buttons and we ascended to Wonderland.

Henry had spent several hours with us, and now must attend to the making of tomorrow's sausages, so, after ushering us into the apartment, he gave Papa written instructions as to how we were to spend the next three days.

None of us had ever been inside an apartment before. Mama and Aunt Julie immediately examined the kitchen, a most unbelievable room the size of a pantry back home. "Look here, Julie," Mama said. "A garbage can IN THE HOUSE." At home all garbage was carted immediately to the chickens. It was never preserved in cans.

Aunt Julie peeked into the tiny cannisters for holding flour, sugar and coffee. "Imagine making a *Kugelhopf* with one cup of flour," she giggled. "How far would it go to making six loaves of bread and a plate of *küchlies?*" At home all staples were kept in large bins.

"No cellar to run up and down for apples, potatoes and carrots," Mama added.

These Californians, they had much to learn it seemed.

It was Mama who made the discovery that there were no beds. We opened the closet doors, thinking one of them must surely yield a secret passage to the bedrooms. One small door hid an ironing board which fell out and hit Uncle Louie on the head.

Papa was examining a paneled wall. "Henry Hockmaier says there are beds called 'Murphy.'" He pulled on a metal handle high in the wall and down crashed the side of the room. Aunt Julie came running from the kitchen. "Earthquake. It is earthquake. Aunt Nace said earthquake happens every day."

"It is only Murphy bed," Papa said.

"Murphy bed," Mama scoffed. "Who but the Irish would think of such a thing. Like a cuttlefish it is." And, indeed, it did look like one, with its soft pink blanket and mattress clinging to the prostrate wall.

"I will not sleep in it," Mama announced.

"Nor I," Julie said. "It might decide to close its shell in middle of the night."

"Well then," Papa said, "Louie and I will take the cuttlefish, which leaves the floor to the women unless we find other beds.

The remaining walls yielded no crustacean marvels, but the buffet in the dining room was found to harbor a mattress for two. That took care of Mama and Aunt Julie. A single bed was coaxed from a bookcase in the hall. This Helena claimed. It seemed for a while that Odile and I would indeed inherit the floor, until Mama discovered two padded window seats in the dining room. Sleeping arrangements, while somewhat crowded, were adequate.

I awakened early the next morning to discover that my window bed was practically under a date tree. The gently swaying fronds, the bouquet of golden fruit at the tree's heart and the sweet narcotic scent over everything gave me a sense of well being, of plenty, of reclining in the abode of milk and honey. So it was with some little effort that I brought myself back to reality and the insistent knocking on the door. Aunt Julie, who was sleeping closest to it, was just getting up, sleepily pulling a flowered robe about her shoulders.

"Yes?" she cried.

"Gabbage," came the answer.

"What is it, please?"

"Any gabbage today?"

"No thank you, we don't want any," Julie cried.

The voice and the knocking were insistent.

Julie fumbled for the doorknob and pulled the door open. There stood a slant-eyed man with hair like patent leather. He wore a white coat. "I come gabbage," he said, advancing.

The only slant-eyed person we knew was the pigtailed Chinese who ran the laundry on Starr Avenue in Toledo. We were all scared of him, having heard tales of how he chased people with his hot flatiron if they argued over the amount of starch in a collar or tried to claim laundry without a "tickee."

Julie backed into the room screaming, while the slant-eyed man came toward her, waving his arms and frantically shrieking, "Gabbage."

Mama came running in from the kitchen. She picked up the handiest object. It happened to be Uncle Louie's camera.

Louie charged out of the living room, pulling suspenders over his nightshirt, just in time to rescue his prized *anastigmat* lens in mid-air.

Papa broke out of the bathroom, razor in hand, his face lathered, only his eyes showing.

The intruder backed out of the door quickly, bowing all the way.

From down the hall we heard the knocking on another door. The call: "Gabbage. Any Gabbage." We heard the click of a can.

Papa went to the open door. He scanned the hall. He closed the door behind him. He eyed Julie and my mother with painful patience. "A working man. A

Japanese working man. He picks up the garbage pails it would seem. And you, Julie, said you wouldn't have any. I must say, although you show little sense, you do have good taste."

Over breakfast, Papa read Henry's plan for us for "Day Number One." In heavy script, on a square of butcher paper, we were instructed to board a rubber-neck automobile which would take us through orange groves, past a studio and along the ocean. "Everything is free," Henry had written and then underlined in heavy black: "Remember to pay for nothing."

"The hot California sun, it must bother Henry's head," Papa said. "Who gives such free trips?"

Uncle Louie, always looking for a bargain, thought it would do no harm to look into the matter.

We were at the appointed corner at ten o'clock, just in time to see two large touring cars pull up to the curb. They had banners along their sides: "Free trip to studio. See the homes of the stars. Look at the ocean."

Quite overcome by the generosity of the Californians, we rushed to get aboard one of them before the stampede which must surely follow. We were a little surprised to note that our driver, who had a face like a water buffalo, was having so much trouble getting people to take the wonderful, free trip. Finally, both autos were filled. By that time we were already acquainted with the couple sitting in the jump seats who were visiting from Peoria, Illinois, and two elderly ladies, "charter members of the Iowa Society of Long Beach," who informed us they had already taken the trip three times.

Our first stop came quickly and it was a surprise, for it was the Kalem Studio. "Why it's just a few blocks from the apartment," Odile cried. A long black automobile, with drawn side curtains, was waiting before the gates.

"That's Mary Miles Minter in the back seat," the Buffalo announced.

"Mary Miles Minter's not with Kalem," Odile corrected.

Buffalo gave her a withering look and pulled away from the curb.

"Aren't we going in?" Odile asked.

One of the "charter members," a sweet old lady with ruching around her throat and violets bobbing on her hat, leaned across to Odile. "It's harder to get inside a studio than it is to break into a bank."

The Buffalo was bellowing at us through a megaphone, pointing out, as he drove, the homes of the stars. It seemed he was the confidante of all of them. "Now on my left is where Chaplin lives. Talked to Charlie just last week. I agreed with him he should do serious drama. On my right you'll see Theda's house." Before we could get a good look, we were cruising past "Nazimova's villa." He drove so fast we were alongside Nazimova's patio while still peering into Theda's bedroom.

While we were to be given just a peek at filmland

and its occupants, it was different when we came to the orange groves. The Buffalo drove right into the center of a big orchard. We were greeted with extravagant hospitality, then told that for the price of fifty cents each we could have our picture taken picking an orange, and we could keep the orange. Business was brisk with all but the "charter ladies" from Iowa. Papa parted with considerable silver since, of course, photographs must be sent to the relatives back home.

Once back in the auto, the Buffalo looked at us fondly. "You're such a good group," he said, "I have decided to give you a special treat. How would you like to see a movie company on location?"

It took a few minutes for the excitement to die down.

"It's a little out of the way," he said. "Hold on."

He left the main road and took a narrow canyon trail which wound through barren rock and was so rough we bounced right off our seats. It was a long ride and Odile, who couldn't stand curves, was just about to get sick when we came out of the canyon onto what looked like pictures I'd seen of the Sahara Desert. The arid land was rimmed by foothills which were like the flanks of sleeping camels. In the distance we could see a stringy fringe of eucalyptus trees blowing in the wind and we were told that the location company was working there.

Odile was the first to spy the group and this was reward indeed for the long, dusty ride. We were not allowed to leave the auto. "Against location rules," the Buffalo said, so we watched from a distance. A camera was set up, manned by a person with his cap on backwards, wearing goggles and puttees. A similarly garbed man sat on a chair and talked into a megaphone. An actor with a mustache was chasing a blonde dressed as a cowgirl with a divided skirt. It was impossible to define her features because her face looked as if she'd fallen into a barrel of flour.

"Who are the stars?" Odile asked.

"Marguerite Clarke and William Desmond," Buffalo said.

"Marguerite Clarke isn't blonde, and Desmond is taller than that."

Buffalo's lower lip quivered. "Those of us in the know understand that the silver screen gives an optical illusion." Without further ado he started the auto and drove away right in the middle of Odile's next question.

His objective was a large khaki tent in a hollow below the trees. Across the front there was a banner. "Welcome to California," it said.

The "charter ladies" hurried to leave the auto. "This is the part we come for," one of them said.

Other autos were there ahead of us, all of them with the "free trip" banners along their sides.

We were ushered inside the faded canvas and seated at long tables set for lunch. We were starving. When plates of sandwiches, macaroni salad and cake were passed, we were impressed. Especially Uncle Louie.

"Imagine, it is all free. I hear all the time that westerners are, how you say it, hospitable, but as much as this I surely did not expect."

After everyone had been lulled into a state of wellbeing by the food, the lazy day and the kindness of the people of the State of California, word spread from table to table that an important personage would tell us a little about our surroundings.

Presently, a large man with a round face, fat hands and blue eyes which disappeared when he laughed and gleamed like agates when he didn't, got up, twirled his wide-brimmed hat, pulled at his flowing black tie, bowed courteously and began: "Unaccustomed as I am to public speaking, I would like to say 'howdy' and 'welcome strangers.'"

We had not been told who this important personage was. Aunt Julie decided he must be the mayor of Los Angeles. Mama thought maybe he was the governor of California.

As he began to speak I noticed several men come through the tent opening and mingle with the tourists. One of them sat down between Papa and Uncle Louie.

The important personage was giving us the history of Los Angeles, telling how it had been a sleepy village until the people from Iowa, from Kansas and from North Dakota had arrived and created a tropic paradise. He gestured through the open flap of the tent. "It looked like the wasteland out there. But do you think this land will be bought to raise oranges, grapefruit and avocados?" He stopped dramatically, then answered his own question. "It is too valuable. But now I have talked enough. I merely wished to welcome you to our glorious state."

A voice piped up from the back of the tent. It came, I noticed, from one of the new men. "Your Honor, is there any chance of ordinary folks, like myself, buying? I've heard a rumor of oil."

The audience buzzed. "Oil! Oil!"

With a great show of reluctance, "His Honor" rose again. "I refuse to say there is oil on this land."

The voice persisted. "You can't deny there is oil in Southern California."

"His Honor" put out his hands in a gesture of helplessness! "I can't deny it."

Another voice was heard. "I, for one, would like the opportunity to get some of this land."

"His Honor" shrugged. "We like to see our native people have first chance. But then, if the rumor is out . . ." He shrugged and sat down.

Whereupon, from all four corners, bright young men emerged with pen and paper. The young man between Papa and Uncle Louie had a map spread out on the table before them. I was glad. Papa already owned stock in a silver mine in Tonopah and shares in a gold mine in Africa. Now we might also own an oil well.

Odile was at times a pain in the neck. This was one

of the times. "Remember what Mr. Hockmaier said. He said not to buy anything."

At that Uncle Louie drew away, but it was too late for Papa. He had signed a piece of paper. I would, it seemed, one day be an oil heiress. Wait until the kids back on Parker Street heard that.

* X *

GOOD AFTERNOON,

MISTER BROWN

* * *

We had not been able to devise a scheme which would open the studio gates to us. And tomorrow we would leave for home. Everyone had given up on the idea excepting Odile. Once Helena had talked Aunt Julie and Mama into joining other tourists in standing in front of the nearby Kalem Studio to watch the stars drive in. They had seen no stars. Just a horse being driven through the gates by a liveried chauffeur.

Odile had spurned the idea of standing at the gates.

She spent every spare moment working over her out-line of "The Clock Strikes Twelve." It seemed a waste of time here in the land of the grapefruit, the avocado and the gardenia to sit in a corner and write about titled Englishmen.

This, our last afternoon, had been set aside by Mama and Aunt Julie to buy souvenirs—an ashtray shaped like a palm tree for Uncle Florival, a sombrero for Uncle Bertie, a satin pillow with a purple painting of Catalina Island for Aunt Marie. Papa and Uncle Louie were inspecting Henry Hockmaier's sausage machinery across the street at the Wiener Wurst.

Helena and Odile had begged to stay in the apart-ment—Helena because she might miss a call from Henry's young friend, the son of his landlady, Bob Rhoades. Since meeting this slim, blond university student, whose hobby was wireless, Helena had com-pletely forsaken her interest in Carlyle Blackwell and the movies. "The boy he comes from a long line of inventors way back to George Washington's time," Henry had told us admiringly. "He spends every min-ute he is not studying, talking to people all over the world."

Since meeting Helena, the world-wide acquain-tanceship of Bob Rhoades must surely have suffered, for it seemed he spent every possible moment ringing our doorbell. Today, Mama and Aunt Julie had no more than left when the doorbell rang and there stood the young student, his blond hair neatly combed back from his serious face. He was tall and slender and he had keen gray eyes and a nice smile that showed even white teeth. He had a box of candy under his arm. "For your train trip," he said handing it to Helena, but including Odile and me in the gift.

I had never seen Helena flustered over a boy before, but now her cheeks were pink, and when Bob Rhoades asked her if she wanted to go for a last walk in the nearby park, she rushed to put on her hat, stopping just long enough to remind us that Mama had said we must not open the door to anyone.

Odile had offered me a dime if I would stay home from the shopping tour and go along with some fantastic plan she had for getting into the Kalem Studio. As soon as we were alone she rushed to the telephone. "Now is the time," she said dramatically.

"You're crazy," I said.

She called a number and, in a very businesslike voice, asked for "Mr. Brown, the story editor."

What she got was his secretary.

Odile's voice was brisk, but her fingers were choking the telephone. "Miss Velda Vaine has the outline of her new scenario ready for Mr. Brown. I'm her assistant. We're leaving for the East tomorrow, so I'd like to make an appointment to show it to him today."

There was a pause, in which I am sure Mr. Brown's secretary rummaged about in her mind for some memory of the famous Miss Vaine. Then the voice distinctly said: "Three o'clock then."

Odile hung up and danced about the room. "Success!" she cried.

"Wait until they see you," I said.

On the trip Odile had been trying to train her hair in a pompadour. Her hair was soft and unmanageable, however, and the pompadour, which should have been a fixed object, was an ever changing phenomenon, beginning the day rolled tightly like one of Mr. Hockmaier's breakfast sausages, but soon shifting to the left or right, and finally slithering down her forehead. It was now at the slithering stage. Odile was always thin, but this summer she was more so. Her face was long and her forehead high. The thinness made one conscious only of her big eyes. It gave her a fragile look which entirely belied her keen sense of business and talent for organization. She appeared helpless when, in fact, she was anything but that.

"Wait until they see you," I said again and I started laughing and couldn't stop. This seemed to urge her to action. She ran to the clothes closet and emerged with Mama's navy tailored dress with buttons to the hem and side panels, the latter, according to the pattern maker, supposedly lending "grace to the walk."

On Mama the hem of the skirt reached the ankles. Odile had grown two more inches this summer and had quite outdistanced my mother so that the skirt hit her just below midcalf.

With the dress my mother wore a white sailor. Odile put it on, stuffing her hair into the high crown, so that only her ears and forehead were exposed. Since she could not get into Mama's high heels, she had to resort to her own vanilla sandals. She didn't look exactly like a gawky girl dressed in her mother's clothes, but rather like a newspaper caricature of a dedicated suffragette.

"We'll have to hurry, it's almost three," she said.

I held back. "Why should I go?"

Odile looked startled, and I realized she was scared. "I need you to carry the manuscript," she said. "That will make it seem more businesslike."

Before leaving, Odile hastily scribbled a note to Mama. "Shatzie and I have an appointment at the Kalem Studio."

Since we did indeed have an appointment, we had no trouble at all getting into the studio office, which faced the street. Odile held me by the hand and her grip was so tight I felt little needles prick my fingers.

Mr. Brown's secretary looked us up, down and sideways. Then she shrugged as if she had seen stranger apparitions come out of the Costume Department, and asked Odile for Velda Vaine's scenario.

We sat on a hard bench waiting while she took the envelope in to Mr. Brown. She gave us another "lifted eyebrow" look as she came out and sat down to her typewriter.

I read a plaque on the wall, an award to Mr. Brown, author of a best seller of the day.

Suddenly the door to the inner sanctum was flung open and a large man with dark, brooding eyes, deeply circled, strode angrily toward the secretary. He had Odile's manuscript in his hand. "What's this . . . ?" he shouted.

The secretary rolled her eyes in our direction.

Mr. Brown approached us as if he were going to snatch us by the scruff of the neck and toss us out the window. I cowered in my chair. He opened his mouth as if to bellow, but the bellow never came. He stared open-mouthed at Odile, whose face was as white as Mama's sailor hat. He closed his mouth and the anger receded from his eyes. The edges of his lips twitched and I thought maybe he was going to laugh, but he didn't. "Which one of you is Miss Vaine's assistant?" he asked.

"I am," Odile quavered.

He looked at me. "Are you another of her assistants?"

"Oh no," Odile said. "She's my little sister. I brought her along because she's never been inside a studio." She looked at me with great condescension. "She's curious. You know how they are at that age!"

"Yes," Mr. Brown said, smiling broadly. "Yes, I know." He bowed courteously. "Will you young ladies kindly step into my office."

We followed him into a handsome room. He asked us to sit down opposite him. We drowned in big black leather chairs while he read "When the Clock Strikes Twelve." He had his back turned. When he swiveled his chair around and faced Odile, his face was serious. "Here at Kalem just now we're filming only westerns. It wouldn't be easy to make 'When the Clock Strikes Twelve' into a western. The Thames would have to be changed to the Snake River or the Gila, and the lords and ladies into cowboys and cowgirls." He looked at

Odile with gravity. "I am sure Miss Velda Vaine would not wish her work tampered with in that way." He leaned closer. "Tell Miss Vaine for me, please, that I think she should keep right on writing, and in a few years when we do something besides westerns she'll be ready for us. We here at Kalem will be looking forward to that day."

Odile stood up, eyes glowing. She thanked Mr. Brown and shook hands. I did likewise. Mr. Brown put a hand on my head, then he addressed Odile. "Perhaps your little sister would like to have a look about our lot."

For a moment Odile's face lit up, then she assumed her brisk manner. "It would indeed be an experience for her."

Then for a full half hour Mr. Brown took us over the lot. We saw a gunfight and a trick horse, and Carlyle Blackwell doing a love scene.

At four o'clock Mr. Brown walked with us to the gates, gave us each a handful of autographed pictures of Kalem stars and waved good-by.

Odile and I were walking on air, so it was with some difficulty that we brought ourselves down to the pavement when we heard, in tones of excitement: "Odile! Shatzie!" There was the family, waiting at the gates through which passed stars and important personages.

We were happy to oblige.

* XI *

THE MATCHMAKERS

* * *

We had returned home from our trip in July. In August, Henry Hockmaier came to Toledo for a visit. Papa said he was not surprised. "It was easy to see he was restless in California. He has there a good business, yet he leaves it and puts it in the hands of his assistant. What is wrong with Henry I do not know. But something it eats at him."

On his arrival, Henry had gone immediately to stay with Cousin Gustave and his wife Anna, and their children Celie and Konrad. They had always been as one big family, having all come to this country together from the same village in Baden.

Henry had stayed on Gustave's farm just one night. Abruptly he had closed his visit and come to stay with us. He didn't seem to know what he wanted. "I think I sell my sausage business in California. I go back to Germany to find a wife," he said.

"Why not find a wife here?" my mother asked. We were at the supper table. Before Henry went to California I had always thought of him as being as old as my uncles. It was because of the big mustache and the stiff black suit. Now that he was clean shaven and wore striped silk shirts I could see that he was just a young fellow—strong, vigorous, with broad shoulders. But now he sat hunched over his plate.

My mother put the question to him again.

"An American wife? They are all like string beans. And what can they do? Helpless they are." He sighed. "I have the strange feeling, here in my chest. It must be *heimweh*."

I knew by this time there was no cure for homesickness but time, and that it was the worst sickness of all.

"Trouble there is in the old country," Papa said. "If war comes you will have to stay over there."

"I think I would like to stay," Henry said sadly, getting up from the table and going outside.

So Mama had called Anna, Gustav's wife, and planned a party. "We must try to find a good sensible

wife for Henry so he will not go back to the old country. We tell all the others."

So Nace had brought her cousin Gretel, large of
hip, strong and healthy. Henry had not given her a
second look. Caeser had brought his sister-in-law, red
cheeked, sturdy, plain Gertrude. Henry had been no
more than polite.

As usual, Gustav's daughter, Celie, was there with
her heart in her eyes. Celie was slender, delicate and
modern. Everyone knew Celie had a crush on Henry
but no one took it seriously because she still wore
middy dresses and her hair down her back. Girls of
marriageable age wore their hair "up."

Henry always noticed Celie, but he noticed her as a
little girl. Earlier in the evening, when he had given us
children nickels "for ice cream at the picnic tomorrow," he had given one to Celie too. She had promptly
thrown it at him.

As usual, over the wine and the *Kugelhopf*, the singing began. Henry didn't have much of a voice but, like
Papa, he "brummed" his way through. Since the party
was for Henry, he was asked to choose the songs. He
called for one sad melody after another. When he
asked for *"Der Tyroler und sein Kind"*—which tells
about going back to the homeland with tears in the
eyes—Uncle Florival stood up and started it in
French: *"Le soir quand j'admire les cieux, Des larmes
perlent dans mes yeux."* My mother and Uncle Louis
joined him, while those who could not sing the French

words hummed the tune. Gustave started the next stanza in German: "*Wenn ich mich nach der Heimat seh'n . . .*" The voices came in strong, for this was an easier tongue for most of the Alsatians, and tonight there were many Germans present. I always sat in a corner with a lump in my throat when they sang these sweet, sad songs. Soft-hearted Aunt Marthe had tears in her eyes as she sang and my mother seemed to be far away in another land. I once asked Uncle Theofil why they sang the sad songs when it made them weep. "My child, give them the chance to weep over the *heimatlieder* and the *wanderlieder* and everybody has the good time," he had answered.

I wondered if Henry was having "the good time." I had seen "wanderers" on the eve of their departure for the homeland. They usually were eager and gay and not at all interested in the sad songs.

Since some relations had to take streetcars home to Ironville, to Point Place and Birmingham, while others went on foot "across the pond," it was still early when the party was over. Gustave and Anna had their team outside to take them back to the farm, but Celie got permission to stay all night.

Celie and I helped Mama do the dishes, while Henry and Papa talked.

"When I get to Germany I will buy a piece of land," Henry said.

"Ha! Ha!" Celie said.

Henry frowned in the way he had with her now, then he smiled indulgently as one does with a child too young to understand. He turned back to Papa and a look of long-suffering patience passed between them.

Papa took his pipe from his mouth. "What is wrong with Henry's buying land in his home village?" he asked. "And maybe marrying a farm girl."

Celie tossed her head so the curls tied with a ribbon at the back of her neck gleamed under the gaslight. "All he wants is a wife he can put to work in the fields and reward on Saturday by allowing her to go into the village marketplace to sell eggs and butter."

"My little one," Henry said. "What can you know of the old country? You were twelve when we left."

"Thirteen," Celie blazed. "You were but five years older. And I have not forgotten the cows next to the kitchen and the manure pile that greets one at the front door. Henry, if you know what is good for you, you will keep your shop in California." She softened. "Look for a girl close at hand."

Henry shuddered. He appealed to Papa. "You know how it is, the unmarried girls who are not betrothed have come to this country because they were too ugly to find husbands in Germany. They are either too old or too sour, or just children as our Celie. Also, when they are here a while they become helpless. After a time they cannot even walk. Always they must take the streetcar. Some of them even talk about buying auto."

Celie looked at me and shook her head. It was indeed hopeless. He would not see her as grown up. He was in fact as much to blame as her parents for her still having to wear middy blouses and pleated skirts. I had heard him talking to Gustave often enough on the subject. "One of the reasons we came to this country is so your children should have their youth." Celie must stay young forever, it seemed. Who would know that she had a slim waist under the bulky middy blouse, or trim ankles under the schoolgirl skirt?

Henry was still telling about the glories of his village in Baden. Celie broke into the conversation. "Let us be finished with this everlasting talk of the old country. Go back. I for one will be happy not to have to listen to you. Now let's plan for the picnic tomorrow at the Pavilion.

Henry laughed. "Hot dogs, popcorn and the Bunny Hug dance they have at the Pavilion. How well I remember the way it was in the old country."

"I suppose you would have us wear leather boots, carry knapsacks and drink goat's milk," Celie said.

Henry's eyes had a faraway look. "And why not?"

Celie's eyes narrowed thoughtfully. "Henry, I do believe that for once you've got a good idea. A picnic the way we did it in the old country."

The next morning when Henry came into the kitchen for coffee and cinnamon rolls he took one look at Celie. "Is masquerade?" he asked.

After early Mass Celie had changed into a green woolen jumper dress that had been my mother's when she was a young girl in the old country. Mama had worn it a few times at reunions in this country when they danced the "Quadrille." With it went a white waist with lots of embroidery and ruffles and a pink scarf that folded about the shoulders and tied in front with ribbons.

Celie twitched her shoulders. "It's from the old country. I wore it for you," she said.

"Very pretty," Henry said. He was holding a handkerchief to his face. "By the way, mantle was missing in bathroom gaslight. Shaving with candle I am not accustomed to."

"There was mantle when I shave," Papa said, motioning Henry to sit up to the table. He passed the cinnamon rolls and Mama poured the coffee.

Celie was tucking a white cloth over the lunch basket. "It is a good thing for a person returning to a farm in Baden to know how to shave by candlelight."

Henry looked at her with suspicion. Then he consulted the clock on the shelf over the roller towel. "Comes time to catch the interurban car," he said.

"You forget," Celie said. "This is an old country style picnic. We walk."

"All the way to the Pavilion?" Henry asked.

" 'It is good for bones. Wonderful for the appetite. It will make roses in our cheeks.' Didn't I hear you say that?"

Henry glanced down at his light-topped patent leather shoes. He shrugged.

Celie handed him the lunch basket.

"Not very heavy," he said. "But then I know you

have fixed good lunch. Last picnic Henriette had fried chicken and chocolate cake. Time before smoked ham and potato salad."

Celie arched her eyebrows. "American style picnics! Today we will have an old country lunch."

Henry looked at Mama. "You are not ready?"

Mama smiled. "We take interurban. But Shatzie, she goes with you."

Henry strode out on the porch. He took a deep breath. "It will be good to walk. Halli Hallo, but it has been a long time since I have walked and practiced yodeling."

Celie's route was more than I had bargained for. It took us over the river by railroad trestle. We ran from a bull when we attempted to cross an inviting meadow and we were chased by a couple of growling sheep dogs when we tried to stop at a farmhouse for a drink of water. By noon Henry hadn't a yodel left in him.

"Celie, are we not soon there?" he asked.

"Oh it's just a little longer," she said.

Henry mopped his face. He forged ahead. Celie looked at me and giggled.

Soon we heard Henry's familiar—"Halli, Hallo." When we caught up he was seated on the bank of a small creek, his bare feet dangling in the water. "Ah, this is good," he sighed. "How far is it yet to the Pavilion would you think? Comes time for a man to eat."

Celie started opening the lunch. "Henry, as you said, in the old country we did not need benches and tables and cold drinks in order to eat lunch. We sat in the woods where it was quiet. We will eat here."

Henry leaned over to have a look at the lunch. Nestling in the bottom of the basket were one yellow cheese and a loaf of black bread. "Sorry, no goat's milk," said Celie, "but we can do as we did in the old country, cup our hands and drink from the stream."

Henry blinked. Then he grinned. "You think I do not know what you do. You try to keep me from leaving. But that is only because I always buy you licorice whips and ice cream sandwiches. That is a selfish reason, Celie."

It was then we heard music. "The Pavilion," Henry cried. He put on his shoes and socks. "Now we can have soda pop. Cold beer. Come, we hurry."

Celie winked at me as she gathered up the lunch basket.

The Pavilion was built out over the water next to a boathouse and concession stand. The relations, gathered under the cool trees eating lunch, called to us as we arrived. We were happy to eat Mama's fried chicken and Anna's cocoanut cake.

Later, we stood along the rail which enclosed the Pavilion dance floor. Henry kept time to the music with his foot. "Celie," he said, "it is right you are. I will agree that some things are good here in America.

"Interurban streetcars do not lose their way in middle of wood, and for picnic I will agree I like fried chicken."

Celie's eyes were shining.

Henry looked at her woolen skirt. Then he looked at the dancers. The music had changed to a waltz. "I think maybe sometimes American dresses are nice too. American waltzes not so bad either." He patted Celie's head and left us abruptly. We watched him walk up to a pretty girl with blond hair dressed in a series of curls on top of her head. She wore a swirling dress of heliotrope voile trimmed with a velvet sash. Hanging from her arm was a horsehair hat from which dangled long velvet streamers.

"It's that man-killer from Ironville," Celie moaned. "She's always been after Henry."

Henry and the man-killer danced by us, dipping and swirling. We could hear the man-killer's taffeta petticoat rustling under the voile dress. Henry didn't look at us.

"Papa won't let me use a powder chamois or wear high heels," Celie said sadly. "If he did, maybe Henry wouldn't think I was a baby. I guess it was kind of silly dressing like this and making Henry walk through the woods. But Shatzie, he's going away. I had to try something," she wailed. Then she grabbed my arm. I looked up and saw that Joe Weber, the saloon keeper's tough son, was coming toward us. "I'm afraid he'll ask me to dance. Papa said I couldn't dance with him." But he didn't. He merely saluted indifferently. Joe was supposed to like them "fancy."

When we turned back to the dancers, Henry and the man-killer were gone.

We left the Pavilion then. The sun was blistering.

"I feel sticky in this outfit," Celie said. We walked toward the river and there before us was the woman's bathhouse and, beyond, the cool river where bathers were splashing about.

"Can you believe it, Shatzie, I've never worn a bathing suit."

"I have," I said. "You can rent them for a quarter at the bathhouse."

"I'm not allowed," Celie said. Her chin went out. "I'm old enough. Come on."

Celie led the way into the bathhouse.

We stood in front of the wavy mirror and looked at ourselves in the suits. I didn't look like much, but I thought Celie looked fine—a little daring perhaps, the white and navy striped dress reached just to her knees. Navy bloomers hung below the skirt, reaching to her nicely rounded calves. The gap between the bloomers and her bathing shoes showed her pretty white skin. She squealed at her image. "I don't dare let Mama and Papa see me."

"Or Henry," I said.

Timidly we poked our heads out of the bathhouse door. The coast was clear. We ran down to the edge of the water and ventured the toes of our laced shoes in its coolness. Then we heard the whistle behind us, and the voice: "Oh you kid."

It was Joe Weber.

"Well, if it isn't little Celie," he said, surprise showing in his broad face. "Say, you're quite a jane. How about going for a ride in my canoe?"

Joe looked coarse in his loud clothes, his straw hat tilted sideways on his big head.

Celie edged away. "Oh, no thanks," she said. But just then a rowboat passed close to the shore. In it was Henry and the man-killer from Ironville. Celie saw them too.

"Oh, come on," Joe was saying. "I'll take you both up to the island and back."

Celie took another look at Henry in the rowboat. She yodeled at him. Henry looked startled for a moment. Then he stopped rowing. "Celie," he cried.

Celie took Joe's arm. "Shatzie and I would love to go to the island," she said.

Celie settled herself in a nest of souvenir pillows in the canoe. She opened the Japanese parasol Joe handed her. He cranked the phonograph. I stood waiting for him to hand me into the canoe. He finally did, but I didn't get the luxury treatment.

Meanwhile Henry was rowing toward us, all the while ordering: "You girls get back on shore."

The canoe cut the water swiftly and soon Henry was left behind. The island was not very far. I was glad. I didn't think I'd care to get too far from the shore with Joe. He always seemed to be leering and his mouth stretched loosely over teeth too small. His hands on the paddle looked white and soft.

When we reached the island, Joe pulled into a cove. The phonograph record had slurped to a stop and the only sound was the water lapping softly against the canoe. "How would you like to explore a little?" he asked me.

Before I could answer he was handing me out of the canoe. Then swiftly he was back in it, shoving away from the shore with his paddle. "We'll pick you up on the way back," he flung over his shoulder.

I was scared.

Celie's face under her bathing cap was white. She closed the parasol and held it like a club.

Just then I saw Henry's rowboat round the point of the island. Almost immediately he was alongside the canoe. "Celie, you get into this rowboat," he ordered.

Celie's color returned with Henry's presence. She shrugged indifferently.

"The lady knows what she wants to do," Joe yelled. "You can take the kid off the island."

Henry grabbed hold of the bow of the canoe. At that, Joe hit Henry over the head with his paddle, causing him to slump into the bottom of the rowboat. Immediately the man-killer from Ironville started screaming. Meanwhile, Celie rose up in the canoe and banged Joe over the shoulders with the parasol. Then she made a flying jump into the rowboat. This caused the canoe to tip over and Joe slid into the water. In the rowboat, Celie grabbed the oars and headed toward the bank and me. I jumped in. She started back to shore. Then we heard the cry: "Help! I'm drowning!" It was Joe. He was floundering in the water, grasping at the floating pillows.

"I guess he can't swim," Celie said. She rowed back to him, grabbed him by the collar and helped him into the boat.

With Henry in the bow groggy, Joe in the stern panting and the man-killer unconscious, Celie rowed ashore.

Mama, Papa, Celie's parents and some of the relatives were waiting at the dock. They had heard the screaming. Gustave shook a finger at Celie in the bathing dress. "Into your clothes," he shouted.

When we came out of the bathhouse, he was waiting. So was Henry.

Gustav took Celie's arm. "We go home. Did you think I was too soft-hearted to use the strap?"

Henry spoke up. "Papa Gustave. Comes the time a girl is too big for the strap."

"What time is that?" Gustave shouted.

Henry looked at Celie with tenderness. "When she can handle two men—one of them a blind fool—a girl and a boat all by herself."

On the way home Celie and Henry sat together on the wicker seat in the interurban. I was in front of them. "Comes the time to say I'm glad to have my eyes opened, glad to know why I have been such a restless one," Henry said.

After that I didn't hear anything more. Because no one was saying anything.

* XII *

AUF WIEDERSEHEN

* * *

It's easy for me to remember the first time I met
Rudy Hoffner. Papa had taken Odile and me to visit
Rudy's uncle, Fred Hoffner, at his fine house across
the Maumee in West Toledo. Mr. Hoffner, whose
name was really von Hoffner, was the big boss at the
railroad shops. He was a fine gentleman with a degree
from the University of Heidelberg. He and his wife,
Loretta, had no children.

Papa would occasionally visit Mr. Hoffner to talk
about matters at the shop which must be done in pri-

vate. On these occasions Papa liked to take one or two of us along—"to show us off." We liked to go. There was always hard candy for us in a heavy cutglass dish, and the goldfish to watch as they swam around the large tank in the conservatory, where it was like summer even in the wintertime, and glass shelves held shiny-leafed begonia plants, schizanthus and lacy ferns which cascaded to the floor like a waterfall.

We would always be asked, during the visit, to play the piano, and we would have practiced a duet, carefully, so as not to make a mistake under the watchful eyes and the keen ears of the Hoffners, especially Mrs. Hoffner, who was a graduate of the conservatory at Leipzig.

Today Papa was taking Odile and me. Mama was supervising our dressing, buttoning Odile into the new blue wool she had made for her. Odile tied the sash to the side. "No, Odile," Mama said. "It must be worn this way," and she took the heavy satin between her quick fingers and tied it into a bow at the back.

Odile considered the sash in the mirror. "I don't like it that way. Tillie Mueller has one like it." Odile could not bear to wear a dress exactly as the pattern designer had decreed, for "who was this unknown person who decreed that all sashes must be worn thus and so this year?" Besides, Tillie was not a favorite of Odile's. The fact that tattle-tale Tillie had a sash at the back was enough to make her dislike all such sashes.

The blue wool on Odile somehow made me take a second look, and I saw that her large eyes were the exact deep blue of the dress, and today I did not think her skin "sallow," but more the color of pale cream. A ridiculous notion took hold of me. Would Odile one day not be so skinny, her hair not so unmanageable? Was it possible that one day she would not be so stubborn and headstrong, and that she too would have beaux like Helena? Oh no, I thought. That could never be. For to have admirers one need have white skin, rosy cheeks, be softly rounded and have masses of curly hair falling about the face. Such being the case, Odile and I were forever doomed to be old maids.

Odile was still arguing about the sash, and I knew that once out of Mama's sight, the sash would be pulled to the side. Odile would have the last word. As for me, I preferred to stay out of trouble. My dress, identical in pattern, was of rose wool. I wore it exactly as the patternmaker and Mama had decreed, sash tied firmly at the back.

Papa helped us into our black plush coats, and we carried the white astrakhan muffs we had gotten for Christmas. Around our black plush hats we tied chiffon scarves to keep our ears warm, for it was a cold day. From our wrists dangled the silver vanities Uncle Louie and Aunt Julie had given us, and we felt quite grown up when Papa took us by the arm and walked us up Parker Street to catch the streetcar.

While Mama reminded us, when necessary, of our

faults, Papa saw only the good in his children. He even liked to brag about us a little.

"Mr. Hoffner will be surprised to see how you have grown since last year," he said. "His nephew, Rudy, visits him from Berlin. You must be extra polite to Rudy."

"Is it true, Papa?" Odile asked. "Will there be war in Europe?"

Papa was always cheerful, but at the mention of war his face saddened. "There is much unrest. But perhaps nothing will come of it."

We were cold by the time we rang the Hoffner doorbell, having had to wait for our transfer at Summit Street, but, as always, the beautiful lace curtain showing through the finely carved oval of the glass door intrigued me with its pattern of roses and sprays of lilies. I did not have long to admire it today for the door was opened quickly and Mr. Hoffner was shaking hands with us, drawing us into the warm room, gravely commenting on the fact that he had expected children, not young ladies. Mrs. Hoffner kissed us. She was one of the few persons we did not mind having kiss us. She was a large soft woman who wore stiff stays to hold in the softness so that she gave the appearance of an unyielding tube, until one became conscious of the delicate fragrance of violets about her and felt the gentle hands smoothing the hair and the soft, though gutteral, voice trying to manage English.

It always gave me a feeling of luxury to sit in the polished mahogany rockers fitted with deep green velvet, to see again the oil paintings in their carved gold frames and to feel the thick red carpet under my feet. Especially did I like being treated as if I were truly grown up.

But today was different. Today these things were not of such importance. Today there was Rudy.

He was standing, smiling, next to the big base-burner as Mrs. Hoffner led us toward him. He was about eighteen, maybe nineteen, I thought. Tall, although not so tall as my father, with thick brown hair, just slightly curly, and such an animated expression on his strong young features, I thought immediately: "I like him."

When his aunt introduced him, he bowed courteously, the way no American boy would think of doing, but through it all his brown eyes held a glint of laughter. In perfect English, with an intriguing accent, he said: "I am honored to meet the American young ladies."

He helped us off with our coats, just as if we were indeed young ladies instead of just girls, Odile fourteen and me eleven, and he did what I had observed only in the movies before—he held our chairs for us, and then he sat on a low hassock between us and gave us his entire attention while Papa and Mr. Hoffner talked about affairs at the railroad shop and Mrs. Hoffner busied herself setting out chocolate drops and bowls of hazelnuts.

At times I could overhear the conversation on the other side of the room, and now it was of war and the uneasiness in Germany and in France, but all of this seemed far away from this warm and sunny parlor, with the fire glowing rosy red behind the isinglass windows of the burner, the soft chairs, and outside the sun on the snow so dazzling bright one could not look at it for long.

But dominating everything was Rudy and his extraordinary vitality, evident in his every gesture and look. It was such a real thing one could almost feel it—it was like the pent-up energy of a young runner waiting at the starting line to begin the race.

I didn't want to talk. I just wanted to listen to this exciting young man speak beautiful English. I was used to the broken talk of some of my relatives, but his were the syllables of the well-trained foreignborn; they were as rough stones polished to a mellow smoothness. He told us about his family in Berlin; his older brother, blond, slim Gottfried, a teacher just recently called into the army; about his mother and the rose arbor in the garden where she served coffee to her friends every afternoon in the good weather. But mostly he talked about his little sister Maria. "She is about your age," he said to Odile. "With eyes the same color as your's. Blue, with a little violet in them —like alyssum."

I had never heard of alyssum, but I knew it must be a lovely flower, for it had such a caressing sound, at least the way Rudy said it.

For a change, Odile was not doing all the talking. Just a question now and then: "Why do you call your schools 'gymnasiums'—why is it you name your classes '*serta, quinta* and *quarta*,'—and is it true you learn Latin at nine years old and French at eleven, and that you have six years of Greek before you enter the university?"

As Odile listened to Rudy there was a soft pink glow in her cheeks. I wondered whether it was from the firelight or from some inner excitement.

After a while, Rudy suggested we take a walk. "You must see the crystal trees."

"Crystal trees?" Odile asked.

"The unseasonable rain of last week, followed by the freeze and the new snow, have made the trees in the ravine a fairyland."

Odile disliked snow and walks in the cold, but now she was the first one on with her rubbers, and when Rudy took our muffs away from us saying, "One cannot walk in a ravine carrying a muff," she did not argue, nor did she dissent when he frowned at our hats and insisted we wear only our scarves. When he inspected our mittens to see whether they were "for show or warmth," I knew the color in Odile's face was not from the fire.

We had to walk fast to keep up with Rudy. He was hatless and he wore a dark blue overcoat, with a white muffler carelessly knotted about his neck. This was the first time anyone like Rudy had paid any attention to Odile and me. A handsome prince walking with two Cinderellas.

We left the sidewalk to take the path behind the

Hoffner house. Here the snow was untrodden. Our rubbers made a squeaking sound as we left our trail of footprints along the edge of the ravine. And then we came upon the trees in the softly sloping hollow. It was breathtaking. We stopped, silent, for a few moments. Here were the tall birch, the sturdy oak, the stately maples, their identities all but lost under their greatcoats of shimmering ice. Rudy led the way. It was so unreal walking beneath the crystal trees, I had the feeling that here was a moment out of time and space, a shining instant to be remembered always.

We left them, reluctantly, to walk along the frozen creek to the other side of the ravine, toward the boisterous cries of boys, and we climbed to the top of the hill to the point of departure for toboggan and racer. We stood watching three boys, in plaid balmacaans and knit caps, maneuver their homemade toboggan down the icy slopes, then labor up the hill to fling themselves down again on the crude boards.

Rudy's eyes flashed. "This is my favorite sport," he said, and he told us a little about tobogganing in Switzerland. "Do you like coasting?" he asked us.

"Oh, I think it is very exciting," Odile said, and I looked at her, for no one had ever been able to get Odile on a toboggan. I was a little scared of them, but Odile was terrified.

The three boys were nearing the top of the hill on the long climb. Rudy hailed the leader. "Young fellow, may we borrow your toboggan for a ride?"

I saw Odile step back a pace as the boy handed over the toboggan, grinning. Rudy grabbed us, none too gently, and sat us down, feet ahead stiffly. In a second we were in swift motion, the wind singing a wild song in our ears, the cold searing our faces. As always, once I got on a toboggan, the fear left me and I tingled with excitement. When we reached the bottom, Rudy sprang up, grabbed us by the hand and pulled us to our feet. "Fun?" he grinned.

"It was wonderful," Odile said, but I saw that her face was white.

"What do you say then we ask the owner of the toboggan if he will allow each of us a turn alone. It is faster that way—flat on the stomach."

Odile's hand went to her mouth. "She's going to be sick," I thought. Rudy turned to look at us. He stopped grinning when he saw Odile, but now she was running ahead, shouting back to us. "I'll be first."

Odile must be first, and she must be best. Even if it killed her. Especially in front of Rudy.

When we reached the top of the hill, Rudy gave the toboggan back to the boy over the protests of Odile. He pulled her scarf back over her hair, for the wind had blown it off. "It is after all a man's sport," he said gently. "My little sister, Maria, does not like the toboggan either."

I saw the anger in Odile's eyes for having been discovered, or was it for having been likened to his "little sister?" But when he tied her scarf more securely under her chin and playfully pinched her cheeks, the anger vanished and her eyes were a lovely blue—and I thought I knew now what alyssum looked like.

When we came again to the trees on the homeward journey, we stopped to once more marvel at them. Rudy grinned like a small boy. "Come, let each of us drop a copper coin, for luck, in the deep snow here under this tall birch. There is a legend: if you find the coins in the spring, after the snows have melted, you will meet once more."

Odile and I had left our vanities behind, so Rudy drew a handful of coins from his pocket. He gave Odile an Indian penny and me one of the new Lincolns. We fell to laughing then for he had no copper coin left for himself. But in another pocket he found a shining new German coin. We inspected it carefully. One side of the copper piece showed the proud German eagle; the other read "2 Pfennigs." The date was 1914.

We dropped the coins close by the trunk of the tree. They fell through the loose snow. Then we stood for a moment looking up at the tall birch. "It will be easy to remember the tree," Odile said. "It is the tallest."

"Shssh," Rudy said. "The trees began to weep." We stood in attitudes of listening, and we heard the noise, like tears splashing. A branch of the birch was bent low under its weight of sparkle, and I saw that it was, indeed, weeping, the ice melting and dripping from the ends of the branches.

"It's so beautiful. Why must it melt," Odile cried.

Rudy shook his head, rubbing a gloved forefinger over a branch of crystal. "Spring must come, and the new leaves, so everything can begin all over again."

It started snowing a little. Some of the flakes caught in his dark hair, and I thought it odd I had never seen snow in a man's hair before. Rudy was still holding the branch between his fingers and for a moment he seemed remote, and I wondered what his thoughts were so far from his homeland.

Then he turned toward us and his eyes gleamed like a small boy's. In a flash he was scooping up handfuls of snow and pelting us. We started to run. We reached the Hoffner front door out of breath and disheveled. Inside, our coats dripped snow water over the red hall carpet. Mrs. Hoffner laughed indulgently and took our wet things to hang in the warm kitchen smelling of nutmeg and baking. Rudy peeled off our rubbers and placed them under the kitchen range.

A table had been set for us in front of the fire. There was a tall pitcher of steaming cocoa, a bowl of whipped cream frosted with cinnamon, a coffee ring still warm from the oven, brown and sugary, gay with flowers of citron and cherries. Mrs. Hoffner bustled over us, pouring the cocoa into thin cups, while in the background the men drank coffee and sipped brandy.

Rudy asked us about school, but now our lives seemed dull to us, and we begged him to tell us about Heidelberg University, which he would enter on his return home. Odile and I shuddered, yet we were excited when he told us of the fencing bouts between the fraternities, and the pride the fencers took in their scars.

And so the afternoon passed and it was time to light the lamps and Papa said we must go.

Rudy held our coats, warm and dry. Just before he slipped Odile's over her shoulders he looked at her dress with the sash tied at the side. "Odile, you should always wear that color. But to my way of thinking, the sash should be tied at the back," and without ceremony he pulled the sash around so the bow was at the back.

I waited to hear Odile argue, but she said only, "Thank you," and then, laughingly, "*Danke schön*."

All the way home, Odile asked Papa questions about Rudy.

"Mr. Hoffner gives him this visit in America before he enters the university. He was as a big brother to you. I always wished for a brother for my girls. We will invite him to supper, with his aunt and uncle, before he leaves for Germany."

They came soon after that, for Rudy had been suddenly called back to Germany for his military service. No mistake, this was special company—the head boss coming to supper with his wife. Mama thought it best to invite Baptiste and Nace, since Baptiste was of next importance to Mr. Hoffner at the shops. We made faces when Mama said this was necessary or Nace would be insulted, for we feared Baptiste a little and we did not care for Nace's sharp tongue.

Mama took no chances on allowing Helena or Odile to concoct the new-fangled dishes they often experimented with, such as fish in quivering jelly, salad bathed in something called mayonnaise or fruit drowned in whipped cream. This was too important an occasion. For this there must be noodles sliced so thinly they were no broader than the edge of her cutting knife and as delicately yellow as a baby chick just out of its shell; goose wearing a crisp brown overcoat to mask its inner tenderness; potatoes boiled with an equal amount of carrots and mashed with butter until they stood a golden mountain on the platter; apples filled with sugar, cinnamon and nuts, roasted, then made into a chaplet around the goose.

The round dining-room table was opened wide, covered with the heavy white damask with scalloped edge. The centerpiece was Mama's butterfly bowl. Odile and I polished the winter fruits—winesap apples, seckel pears, and, extravagantly, Tokay grapes from California which had come packed in sawdust. In the other we placed all manner of nuts, shined until they gleamed like wood.

The supper was on a Saturday, the same night that Odile's and Helena's dancing class was having its "final party with escorts." Odile was not going.

Rudy sat between Odile and Helena at the table. Helena was already dressed for the party in her red taffeta. She had a black velvet ribbon around her hair and she looked so pretty and gay. I thought, Rudy will fall in love with Helena tonight.

Nace, in her black satin with the boned neck, looked stiffer than ever. She watched as Rudy talked to Helena and Odile, and frowned at Odile's giggling. Giggling was rare in Odile. Tonight she giggled at almost everything Rudy said.

Nace was not fond of Odile because Odile would not hold her tongue when Nace was critical. We had reached the dessert when Nace got Odile's attention. "It is too bad you are not going to the dancing class ball. Could you then not find a boy to take you?"

Odile's face turned red as the winter apples in the butterfly bowl. Helena, usually docile when Nace was around, gave Nace an impudent look. "Odile doesn't care much for dances," she said.

Nace smirked. "Of course not. Of course not. We all know Odile does not care for dancing or for the boys." Her tone implied that it was the boys who did not care for Odile.

My father, slow to show anger, and never when company was present, shifted in his chair. Two pink spots glowed on his cheeks. My mother's green eyes were flashing.

Rudy looked for a long moment at Nace. Then he turned to Odile. "So, you would not ask me, your new friend, to go to the ball."

Odile, who had been sitting through all this with lowered eyes, now shot a suspicious look at him. "It's not a ball. It's just a party to celebrate the last lesson of dancing class."

"I must say my little sister Maria is more thoughtful.

She has asked me to accompany her to her first dances."

He looked at the others around the table. "I have never been to an American dance. I must leave for Germany in a few days, and yet this American girl refuses to invite me."

Odile glanced quickly at Rudy as if she expected him to be laughing. He was sulking.

Mr. Hoffner started talking then about matters at the shop, and while everyone made a pretense of listening, looks were darted Rudy's way. I was surely surprised to see the handsomest man I had ever met brooding because Odile had not asked him to the dance. I pictured the boys Odile might have asked if she had had the courage—Dutch Schultz, Loud Mouth Kelling, Ignatz the Goat, Emil the Dutchman. Of course there was nice Walter Keesling, but he had broken a leg ice skating down at the pond.

I saw Helena gesturing to Odile behind Rudy's back, her lips forming the words: "Ask him. Ask him."

Odile shook her head. Then she stole a glance at the "injured" Rudy. Bashfully she put her hand on his arm and said something.

Rudy's smile was instant. He jumped up from the table and stood behind Odile's chair. "The sphinx has spoken," he said to the gaping circle. "Come Odile, you must waltz with me around the parlor. You see, I can dance only the German steps. You must teach me the American way."

Everyone broke into grins, even Nace. I saw my father's gaze meet Rudy's across the table. If Rudy were his son, he could not have shown greater affection.

Helena's date, a senior from St. Ignatius, arrived. They decided to practice their steps too, so the four of them danced to music from the phonograph, while from behind the French doors the supper guests lingered over coffee and stole secret looks. Odile might be gangling but, being Odile, she had learned to dance well. I could not help wonder at the stir they would make at the party, my awkward sister and this vital, polished and handsome prince.

The grownups played pinochle until eleven o'clock, the hour the dancers were to return. I was allowed to be scorekeeper and put down the melds and the bids.

They came home, the four of them, all excited. The dancing master, having learned Rudy was from Germany, had asked him to dance the German waltz with Odile. Then everyone wanted to learn it. "They did four exhibition dances," Helena said. Odile's eyes were glowing. I looked at the dance program dangling from her wrist. It was crowded with names. Odile had on a powder blue taffeta party dress Mama had made. It had blue lace at the throat and bands of it in the full skirt. She wore a pale blue ribbon in her hair, and I thought: "She *will* be pretty one day."

And then we were saying good-by to the Hoffners, but especially to Rudy. "The trouble over there will not last long," he said with assurance. "My brother

Gottfried writes it will amount to nothing." Looking at him, so vital, so strong, I was sure he could right things singlehandedly.

Rudy kissed us all good-by. When he leaned down to kiss Odile he took both her hands in his, and in that brief moment of parting I thought I saw an awakening in his eyes, as if perhaps he were not seeing Odile as she was now, at fourteen, all angles and eagerness and reminding him of his little sister, but Odile perhaps at eighteen, soft and wise.

"You'll write?" she asked.

"Yes," he said, and he kissed her a second time. This time on the mouth. "*Auf Wiedersehen*," he said.

And then we were all saying it: "*Auf Wiedersehen, Auf Weidersehen*," the words which say good-by while promising a future rendezvous; words which at this time and place said all and enough, if they would come true.

Another spring had come.

We were again at the Hoffners—Mama, Papa, Helena, Odile and me. This time we had come because of the problems brought about by the war in Germany, and because of Mr. Hoffner's personal loss.

The Hoffners met us at their lace curtained door. Their smiles were warm, but sad. The candies and the nuts were waiting, as usual, and the fish in the conservatory. But we did not eat, nor did we look. Our eyes were on the black-rimmed letter lying on a mahogany table next to the morning paper whose headline screamed: "Further atrocities attributed to the Germans."

Mr. Hoffner read to us from the letter. It was from his brother and had reached him via Switzerland:

"My eldest son, Gottfried, was killed in the first battle. Rudy, my youngest has not been heard from since the Battle of the Marne. . . ."

When he finished, the sunny room seemed bleak. Mr. Hoffner wept openly and so did Mrs. Hoffner and my parents. Soft-hearted Helena sobbed out loud. I felt a hurt in my throat. Odile ran out of the room. I hurried after her.

It was a beautiful warm day in the ravine, with the smell of spring and the first violets. We had no trouble finding the birch. The winter's snows were long since gone, and wild grass grew beneath it. Without a word we got down on our knees to search. I had long given up, but Odile was still looking for the three copper pennies—one Indian, one Lincoln, the third a German two-pfennig piece. Over a year had passed since we had dropped them into the snow, and in that time many snows had come and melted, forming rivulets which grew in volume as they coursed down the ravine, washing before them everything in their path in the rush to the boiling stream below. I knew our coins must be somewhere in that swollen stream. It was hard to believe it would be smooth as pond water again.

When I turned to Odile she was no longer searching. She reached up and pulled down one of the branches of the tree. It was covered with tiny, silken buds. I remembered what Rudy had said: "Spring must come, and the new leaves, so everything can begin all over again." Odile held the branch next to her cheek and I saw something in her face I had never seen before. A matureness. I knew instinctively that I would never see her quite as she had been, the crazy Odile with the crazy ideas and the crazy dreams.

I thought of other things that were gone—Rudy, with the snow clinging to his dark hair. Peace was gone. The world was like the raging stream below.

And then I thought of my family. Papa was German. Mama's heart was French. It was as if the war would come inside our house. I started to sob out loud for suddenly the weight of all the troubles in the world was here with me. I ran toward the house. I stumbled and fell.

It was then that I felt Odile's arms around me. She pulled me to my feet. I had not realized her arms were so strong. "Wipe your eyes, Shatzie," she said. "The ones in the house feel badly enough. Wipe your eyes. We must go in."

✳ XIII ✳

ON THE WING

* * *

I had never gone back to the ravine. I knew the birch
had leafed and thrown its shade for a brief summer,
and now, judging by the cherry tree I was even now
looking at, must once more be bare, waiting for the
snows and then again the spring, so, as Rudy had said,
"everything can begin all over again." I knew that
Odile had gone into the ravine when we were at the
Hoffners. I wondered if she still searched for the
copper pennies.

Yes, spring would come and the cocoon in the cherry tree would yield its butterfly. There was a way to hurry the process and Nace had shown it to me. She had brought a cocoon into her warm kitchen and put it near the stove. In a surprisingly short time the butterfly had begun to emerge. I had watched with her. It was one of the large butterflies with exotic markings, but now its wings were damp, folded to its sides, as it groped its way. As its wings dried, the butterfly tried to spread them, then when they were at their fullest and it seemed about to fly Nace had applied the chloroform and the butterfly had been arrested in its first flight. Nace stuck a pin through its head and attached it to one of the lace curtains in her parlor. It had made me sad. I knew the life of a butterfly was short, but this one had been denied even that little while. The smell of chloroform had sickened me and I had gone from Nace's spotless house and since then had avoided looking at the butterfly on the curtain.

It disturbed me now, remembering what Odile had written in her diary about this being the Year of the Butterfly. In emerging from their cocoons then, would any of them be "pinned to a lace curtain?"

I knew the relations had arrived for I could hear the talking through the storm windows. Uncle Benedict's Carl was even now calling my name. He had a mother now. Rosalie. We had learned so much from her in the past year.

I went in then. Everyone was there. Well, almost

everyone, things being the way they were. Deesie was striding up and down the living room. He had long arms and short legs. His Sunday suit coat came almost to his knees. "I am standing in saloon eating the free lunch, drinking a glass of beer," he said. "I am telling the bartender not to believe everything he reads in the newspaper about the Germans, when comes this man up to me and cries. 'If you like Germany so well, why don't you go back? Germans are dogs.' So what do I do? I hit him. What happens next? In comes policeman. He puts me in wagon. Next thing I am in jail. Me, Deesie, who never as much as broke one law in his life."

"Then what?" Papa asked.

"When I go before the judge I tell him my father he is over ninety years old and lives in Schleswig-Holstein and he is not a man to cut off the hands of children as the newspaper says. I tell him my brother in Westphalia is too soft-hearted to wring the neck of a chicken. I tell him they are not dogs."

My father took his cigar from his mouth. "Go on," he said.

"The judge he lets me go, but first he says: 'Keep your mouth shut. No matter what anyone says to you, keep your mouth shut.' "

Deesie put his hands out in a gesture of appeal. "Am I then to listen to lies and say nothing?"

Gustave spoke up. "Yesterday I stop by a house over on Willard Street where I always deliver sweet butter. The lady of the house she comes to the door and she says, 'No, thank you,' and slams it in my face. When I get back to my wagon her boys have put a sign on the back of it: TO HELL WITH THE KAISER."

Uncle Florival jumped to his feet. "And I say so too. I do not say, Gustave, that it was right for the boys to put the sign on your wagon, but I also say TO HELL WITH THE KAISER. We Alsatians have suffered long enough. Germany has held Alsace hostage since 1871. Our father, who fought against Bismarck, predicted the day of the liberation would come. I say France is right. Germany is wrong."

Deesie strode up to Florival and grabbed his lapels. "Alsace belongs to Germany by right."

Florival tried to shake him loose. "Not by right, by might," he shouted.

My mother appealed to my father. "Do something, Herman."

My father strode across the room and pushed the two men apart. "We settle nothing this way."

Deesie stomped to the door. "I will not stay here to be insulted."

Uncle Louie barred his way. "You stay. We settle this. We are split apart politically, true. But we can settle things between us."

Everyone was talking. Arms were waving.

My father walked to the center of the room. "QUIET, all of you," he shouted. It was a rare thing for my father to shout. The room became still immediately.

"First it would be well for all of us to remember what St. Augustine has said: 'War is not between people. It is between countries.' "

Deesie started to say something. "Quiet, Deesie," my father said.

"I also have a father in Germany. He too is over ninety years old. Do you think I do not remember he is kind and good? Now what do you think he hears in my home village? He hears only stories of the atrocities of the French. We must all remember that propaganda is just a different kind of ammunition. Anyone who understands human nature must know that men are men the world over."

"No one wishes to believe the truth," Gustave said sadly.

"And what is the truth?" Papa asked. "The truth for us here and now? Why do you argue, relative against relative, friend against friend? Is it to prove the Germans are guiltless, or that the French have the right? The truth is we are citizens of America and that up until now we have taken everything this country has offered. The truth is, that should there be war, we must start giving." He turned to Deesie. "Why did you come to America?"

"I was the third son and so could not inherit my father's farm. It must go to the eldest. I came to own land."

Papa turned to Florival. "How did it happen you came?"

"As an Alsatian it galled me to serve in the German

army. I ran away to France. After serving in the
Foreign Legion it strikes me that America is a good
place to make new start."

Gustave broke into the conversation. "I came so my
children could have it better, so they must not stay
shackled in the same class into which they were born."
He looked over at his son, Konrad. "For him I want
more education than eight years in the *Volkschule*.
For my Konrad there must be more than being ap-
prenticed at thirteen."

Papa smiled at Gustave. "For all these things we
must pay."

Konrad was a good-looking, clear eyed boy. "I'll
be old enough to volunteer if there's war in this country," he said spiritedly.

"Our Konrad may be an American soldier?" Anna
wiped her eyes.

"Yes and there will be others if war comes," my
mother said. "Lily's sons, they are seventeen and eighteen.

The room was quiet. "You see," Papa said. "Our
way is clear."

Deesie stalked through the door. "I, fortunately am
a bachelor. Perhaps I will go back to Germany to
fight."

"If he must go, let him," my father said. "Perhaps he
will think it over."

Gloom invaded the room and crowded it. My father
broke the silence. "It is not always easy to give up

one's homeland. We have all known the heartache of it. We must not think too bitterly of Deesie. He has, after all, no family to help him make the new life; no children to watch grow in the new ways, and so make the sacrifice worthwhile."

Everyone looked crestfallen. Aunt Marthe sniffled. Would they ever be happy again? I wondered. Would they ever sing again?

The telephone rang. Odile answered. "Helena, Helena," she cried. "Long distance from California."

Helena rushed down from upstairs. "It's your sweetheart from out in the West," Uncle Bertie joked. The aunts buzzed with excitement.

It was immediately evident that a conversation of importance was taking place. Helena's cheeks were pink, her eyes dancing. The room hung on her every word and gesture. Finally she hung up the receiver softly, dreamily, in another world. We waited breathlessly. She looked at us waiting and burst into tears.

Helena was Uncle Theofil's favorite. "So this genius from California makes you weep. I will tear him apart."

But now we saw that Helena was laughing all the while the tears were rolling down her face. She ran to Mama and Papa. "Bob wants to buy me a diamond. We're engaged."

"A diamond," Uncle Theofil cried. "Is he then made of money? It strikes me it would be more sensible for a bridegroom to buy pots and pans and a washing machine, instead of diamonds." Uncle Theofil was a little jealous of Helena's boy friends.

Aunt Marie gave him a scalding look. "Every American girl gets a diamond when she's engaged."

The aunts clustered around Helena. "I have already embroidered twelve huck towels for your hope chest," Marthe said.

"And I have hemstitched sheets," Aunt Lily said.

"Oh Yerra! so many things, where will she keep them all?" Aunt Marie said, and she gave Uncle Theofil another look.

Theofil grinned then. "I buy you the best cedar chest in Kobackers. After all, you are my godchild."

Papa looked a little sad. "When you think you get married? Not too soon, I hope."

"Of course not, Papa. Bob still has six months' college left. And then he'll have to get a job."

Papa brightened. "Foolish it would be to marry the boy while he still studies. Better to marry the man."

Helena turned back to the telephone. "Before I do another thing I must call the sisters at the academy. They'll be so excited and will want to hear all about it. After that I'll phone some of the girls to come over."

While Helena was telephoning the aunts started making all sorts of plans. "I offer you the farm for the wedding dinner," Anna said to my mother. "There we can sing all the old songs."

Until now Odile had said nothing. Now she raised

her voice. "There's a right and a wrong way to do things. It's lucky I've studied up on wedding etiquette. First we must think of the engagement party."

Aunt Marthe grinned. "Is it that you would like to borrow little Caeser's train for the decorations?"

Everyone laughed. Odile had never lived down the giveaway party she had given for Helena.

"What will you serve?" Aunt Julie asked. "I read of a recipe just right for one of your parties—slice of angelfood cake is supposed to look like piece of bread. On top goes peach which looks like egg yolk, then whipped cream which looks like egg white. Breakfast everyone thinks he's getting. Surprise, it is dessert."

Odile grimaced. "I want to give the party at the Secor Hotel."

"The Secor? Oh Yerra!"

Uncle Louie waved his arms. "What kind of expensive nonsense are you talking?"

Odile raised her eyebrows. "This isn't Alsace. When a girl marries here she has a fancy engagement party, and then all the bridesmaids give parties and showers."

"Bridesmaids?" Uncle Florival shouted. "How many does it take?" In Alsace a girl asked only her best friend to "stand up" for her.

Odile appealed to Mama and she quieted the uncles quickly with one of her fiery looks. She put her hand on my father's coat sleeve. "Helena is the first of the second generation to marry," she said, and her face for a moment was sad. Then her eyes glowed golden green, like spring in the cherry trees. "When the time comes, Helena will have a good American wedding." My father nodded.

Through the living-room window now I saw Walter Keesling, dressed in a neat blue serge suit, coming up the front walk. He ran his hand over his hair and straightened his tie. Odile's glance met mine. I grinned. "You're being silly, Shatzie," she said, but she blushed as she went to the door.

Helena's girl friends began to arrive then, some with boys in tow, and there was much squealing and giggling in the parlor as they surrounded Helena and asked questions, while the older folks sat in the sitting room. Konrad brought out his accordion and played "Here Comes the Bride." That started everyone cheering and Papa said he guessed it was time to go down into the cellar for wine to toast Helena.

"No wine for the young crowd," Odile said. "They'll like Boston coolers." She turned to me. "I'll ask Walter to go to the corner store with me for ice cream. Meanwhile will you get out Mama's lemonade glasses? The tall ones. Boston coolers are the very latest thing to serve. You put a scoop of ice cream in each glass, then fill it up with ginger ale. Very smart."

Father Kelmer came in the door then and everybody stood up respectfully. "Sit down, sit down," he cried. "Tell me what is this I hear about Quicksilver?" So the news was traveling. Helena came out of the parlor shyly and he pinched her cheek, wished her well and sent her back to the young people.

By this time there were so many young people, the older folks gave up the living room and moved into the dining room. For the first time in our house, the young people were in the foreground. The older folks in the background. I thought maybe they didn't mind. They had gone as far as they could in being Americans —the rest of it they must live in their children. It came to me that the hurt of the older ones about the war in the homeland would be less bitter because their children were not a part of it and had no feeling for that homeland. They, the parents, had so willed it years ago when they had come to America.

The butterflies are on the wing, I thought. I stood for a moment at the dining-room window and looked up into the cherry tree at the cocoon, wondering what kind of butterfly would emerge from it. A plain little one maybe, content with the honeysuckle and the roses in the garden. Or would it be a large, exciting one that must fly far and high to exotic blooms, not knowing what butterfly nets might greet it or what striped cat might be waiting?

It was comforting to know that I was just the plain kind, the kind no one tried to catch, and certainly never pinned to a lace curtain.

I turned back to the older folks just in time to hear Uncle Florival say, "For Helena we must sing some of our love songs. This second generation does not really know what a good love song is. We start with: '*Du, du liegst mir in herzen.*' "

As their voices rose in harmony, I saw content in their faces. I went into the kitchen and started preparing the Boston coolers. *"Du, du, liegst mir in herzen,"* I hummed the old tune, as I made the smart modern drink.